Cambridge Tracts in Mathematics and Mathematical Physics

GENERAL EDITORS

J. G. LEATHEM, M.A.
E. T. WHITTAKER, M.A., F.R.S.

No. 4

The Axioms of Projective Geometry

THE AXIOMS OF
PROJECTIVE GEOMETRY

by

A. N. WHITEHEAD, Sc.D., F.R.S.

Fellow of Trinity College

HAFNER PUBLISHING COMPANY
New York
1971

Reprinted by Arrangement
with the
Cambridge University Press

Published by
HAFNER PUBLISHING COMPANY, INC.
866 Third Avenue
New York. N.Y. 10022

Library of Congress Catalog Card Number 60-11042

Printed in the U.S.A.

Noble Offset Printers, Inc.
New York, N.Y. 10003

PREFACE

IN this tract only the outlines of the subject are dealt with. Accordingly I have endeavoured to avoid reasoning dependent upon the mere wording and on the exact forms of the axioms (which can be indefinitely varied), and have concentrated attention upon certain questions which demand consideration however the axioms are phrased.

Every group of the axioms is designed to secure the deduction of a certain group of properties. For the most part I have stated without proof the leading immediate consequences of the various groups. Also I have ignored most of the independence theorems, as being dependent upon mere questions of phrasing, and have only investigated those which appear to me to embody the essence of the subject; though, as far as I know, no formal line can be drawn between these two classes of theorems.

But there is one group of deductions which cannot be ignored in any consideration of the principles of Projective Geometry. I refer to the theorems, by which it is proved that numerical coordinates, with the usual properties, can be defined without the introduction of distance as a fundamental idea. The establishment of this result is one of the triumphs of modern mathematical thought. It has been achieved by the development of one of the many brilliant geometrical conceptions which we owe to the genius of von Staudt. The definitions of distance and of congruence, and the proof of the existence of groups of 'congruence-transformations,' are reserved for a subsequent tract upon Descriptive Geometry. But these questions are dependent upon the previous introduction of numerical coordinates.

For a full consideration of the various logical and philosophical enquiries suggested by this subject, I must refer to Mr Bertrand Russell's *Principles of Mathematics*. I need hardly say that the formal references in the sequel do not exhaust the extent of my obligations to him.

A. N. W.

CAMBRIDGE,
October, 1906.

CONTENTS

CHAPTER I

FUNDAMENTAL CONSIDERATIONS

1. The present tract on Projective Geometry is designed as a supplement to an advanced school course of Geometry. It is also meant to serve as an introduction to a detailed study of the various questions connected with special systems of projective axioms. In conformity with these objects an elaborate study of one special system of axioms is not undertaken. Such a system is given here : it serves as an example, and also as a text, upon which is based a discussion of the various leading ideas which have to be taken account of in any system of Geometrical axioms. It is hoped that a student, who is acquainted with the discussion here given, will be able at once to recognize the relation to the subject as a whole of the various detached memoirs upon it.

A succeeding tract will deal upon the same plan with Descriptive Geometry, including Ideal Points, Congruence, and Distance. None of these topics are considered in the present tract which ends with the introduction of numerical coordinates into Projective Geometry.

2. Geometry, in the sense in which it is here considered, is a part of Pure Mathematics, and like all such sciences it is composed of Definitions, Axioms, Existence Theorems, and Deductions. Here 'Definition' will always be used in the sense of 'Nominal Definition,' that is, as the assignment of a short name to a lengthy complex of ideas. Accordingly, in this sense, the definitions are no essential part of the subject. The geometrical axioms are statements about relations between points ; but they are not statements about particular relations between particular points. The class of points and their relations are not otherwise specified than by the supposition that the axioms are true propositions when they are considered as referring to them.

1

Thus the points mentioned in the axioms are not a special determinate class of entities; but they are in fact any entities whatever, which happen to be inter-related in such a manner, that the axioms are true when they are considered as referring to those entities and their inter-relations. Accordingly—since the class of points is undetermined—the axioms are not propositions at all : they are propositional functions*. An axiom (in this sense) since it is not a proposition can neither be true nor false. The Existence Theorem for a set of axioms is the proposition that there are entities so inter-related, that the axioms become true propositions, when the points are determined to be these entities and the relations between points to be these inter-relations. An Existence Theorem may be deduced from purely logical premises ; it is then a theorem of Pure Mathematics ; or it may be believed as an induction from experience, it is then a theorem of Physical Science. There is a tendency to confuse axioms with existence theorems owing to the fact that, rightly enough, Geometry in its elementary stages is taught as a physical science. Some authors term the axioms 'definitions' of the undetermined entities to which they refer. The enunciation of axioms is then said to be the process of 'definition by postulates.' There is no objection to this phraseology, so long as it is clearly understood that in general— and certainly in Geometry—the axioms do not characterize one unique class of entities (the points); but that many—indeed an indefinite number—of determinations of the class of points are possible, consistently with the truth of the axioms†.

The Deductions are the ordinary propositions of Geometry. It is habitual—and convenient—to enunciate these propositions in an inaccurate abbreviated form. The true form is 'Such and such axioms respecting points imply such and such conclusions'; but in practice the protasis is always omitted. Thus instead of 'Such and such axioms imply that the angles at the base of an isosceles triangle are equal,' we find, 'the angles at the base of an isosceles triangle are equal.' The deductions do not assume the existence theorem : but if the existence theorem is untrue, the protasis in the deduction is false whatever entities the points are determined to be. The proposition is then true but trivial.

But if we abandon the strictly logical point of view, the definitions—

---

* Cf. Russell, *Principles of Mathematics*, for a complete exposition of this whole question, especially § 13 and Chapter I, and § 353.

† Cf. Russell, *Principles of Mathematics*, § 108.

though in form they remain the mere assignment of names—are at once seen to be the most important part of the subject. The act of assigning names is in fact the act of choosing the various complex ideas which are to be the special objects of study. The whole subject depends upon such a choice. Furthermore, what is in truth an alteration of the axioms and deductions may present itself in practice as an alteration of the definitions. For example, if the axioms involving the word 'plane' are left unaltered, while the definition of 'plane' is changed, the axioms are in effect altered.

There is a gain in the economy of the material employed when the number of undetermined fundamental classes, such as points and straight lines, is reduced to a minimum.

The requisites for the axioms are various. They should be simple, in the sense that each axiom should enunciate one and only one statement. A simple axiom is not necessarily easy to apprehend. The total number of axioms should be few. A set of axioms must be consistent, that is to say, it must not be possible to deduce the contradictory of any axiom from the other axioms. According to the logical 'Law of Contradiction,' a set of entities cannot satisfy inconsistent axioms. Thus the existence theorem for a set of axioms proves their consistency. Seemingly this is the only possible method of proof of consistency. But the only rigid proofs of existence theorems are those which are deductions from the premises of formal Logic. Thus there can be no formal proof of the consistency of the logical premises themselves. This is only one instance of the absolute distinction between the premises of Logic, which are necessary for reasoning itself, and the axioms of various mathematical subjects, such as Geometry or the Theory of Magnitude, which occur as propositional functions in the hypotheses of the deductions of these subjects. These deductions are redeemed from triviality by the belief in the existence theorem for the axioms in question, which is arrived at by formal reasoning or by some vaguer method. Some mathematicians solve the difficult problem of existence theorems by assuming the converse relation between existence theorems and consistency, namely that, if a set of axioms are consistent, there exists a set of entities satisfying them. Then consistency can only be guaranteed by a direct appeal to intuition, and by the fact that no contradiction has hitherto been deduced from the axioms. Such a procedure in the deduction of existence theorems seems to be founded on a rash reliance on a particular philosophical doctrine respecting the creative activity of the mind. But apart from its logical justification the procedure is in practice often wise ; since simple axioms which appear to be consistent probably are consistent, and as far as we know existence theorems can probably be found for consistent axioms. Accordingly it is not well to be hampered in the initial development of a new subject by the lack of the existence theorem and of the attendant proof of consistency.

Practically all the existence theorems of Geometry are derived from developments of the theory of number, namely, of integral numbers, of rational numbers, of real numbers, and of complex numbers. It is widely believed that an inductive proof can also be derived from Physical Science.

A set of axioms should be independent, that is to say, the modified set found by omitting any axiom and by adding its contradictory should be consistent. Thus, according to what has been said above, the proof of the independence of a set of axioms is in fact the proof of the existence theorem for the modified set.

It will be recognized that the really essential logical requisites respecting the foundations of a mathematical subject are that the axioms should be consistent, and that their existence theorem should be proved. Also, owing to the Law of Contradiction, both requisites are secured by the proof of the existence theorem. All the other desiderata—important though they be—are merely logical elegancies, and an excessive insistence on them may do harm in checking the production of creative ideas in the subject.

3. Geometry, in the widest sense in which it is used by modern mathematicians, is a department of what in a certain sense may be called the general science of classification. This general science may be defined thus : given any class of entities K, the subclasses of K form a new class of classes, the science of classification is the study of sets of classes selected from this new class so as to possess certain assigned properties. For example, in the traditional Aristotelian branch of classification by species and genera, the selected set from the class of subclasses of K are (1) to be mutually exclusive, and (2) to exhaust K; the subclasses of this set are the genera of K; then each genus is to be classified according to the above rule, the genera of the various genera of K being called the various species of K; and so on for subspecies, etc. The importance of this process of classification is obvious, and is sufficiently emphasized by writers on Logic. If the genera are defined not as subclasses of K, but as classes with the corresponding species for their members, *i.e.* as classes of classes, and the species as classes with the corresponding subspecies for their members, and so on, till the lowest type of subspecies have members of K for their members, we obtain a hierarchy of classes which it is essential to consider in dealing with the general theory of cardinal numbers. This fact illustrates further the importance of this traditional system.

The Geometrical system of classification is yet more rich in intrinsic mathematical properties, and dominates all external existence.

Geometry is the science of cross classification. The fundamental class K, is the class of points; the selected set of subclasses of K is the class of (straight) lines. This set of subclasses is to be such that any two points lie on one and only one line, and that any line possesses at least three points. These properties of straight lines represent the properties which are common to all branches of the science which usage terms Geometrical, when the modern Geometries with finite numbers of points are taken account of. But no interesting general Geometric science exists in which no other axioms are assumed. The interest of Geometry lies entirely in the development and comparison of its various branches. Most of the important Geometries include, either as an undefined fundamental relation or as a relation defined in terms of the fundamental concepts, the idea of the order of points on a line. Now a linear sequence (or series) can be either open or closed. A closed series returns into itself, like the points on the circumference of a circle; an open series does not return into itself, like the series of integers arranged in ascending order of magnitude. The leading division in those Geometries, which include the order of points on lines, arises according as the straight lines are taken to be open series, or closed series.

A definition of a plane can be given which holds for every geometry, namely : If A, B, C are three non-collinear points, the plane ABC is the class of points, such as X, which satisfies the condition that some line through X intersects at least two of the lines BC, CA, AB, not at A or B or C. But this definition is unnecessarily clumsy in particular Geometries, and can be replaced by more suitable special forms. Also one or more axioms respecting the intersection of lines in planes are required. Here again a division among Geometries is reached, according as any two coplanar lines are, or are not, necessarily to intersect.

A Geometry will be called 'Projective' if two coplanar lines necessarily intersect. Thus Euclidean Geometry is not projective, but becomes so when the various entities called the points at infinity on the various lines have been defined, and added to the other points on the lines.

It will be found that the appropriate kind of linear order for a projective geometry is that of a closed series. A non-projective Geometry will be called a Descriptive Geometry. The appropriate kind of linear order for a descriptive geometry is that of an open series. In Projective Geometry the subject viewed simply as a study of classification has great interest. Thus in the foundations of the subject this conception is emphasized, while the introduction of 'order' is deferred. The opposite course is taken in Descriptive Geometry since the purely classificatory part of the subject is clumsy and uninteresting.

CHAPTER II

AXIOMS OF CLASSIFICATION

4. Throughout the rest of this tract we are concerned solely with Projective Geometry. Thus, following the careful method of enunciation of the Italian school of writers on this subject*, we take as undefined ideas that of 'a point,' and that of 'a line † joining a point A with a point B'; also the line joining A with B will be denoted by AB. Then the following axioms are to be assumed :

I. Points form a class of entities.

II. There is at least one point.

III. If A is a point, there is a point not identical with A.

IV. and V. If A and B are distinct points, the line AB is a class, and all its members are points.

VI. If A and B are distinct points, the line AB is contained in the line BA.

VII. If A and B are distinct points, A is a member of the line AB.

VIII. If A and B are distinct points, the line AB possesses at least one point distinct from A and B.

IX. If A and B are distinct points, and C is a point, distinct from A, lying on the line AB, then B lies on the line AC.

X. If A and B are distinct points, and C is a point, distinct from A, lying on the line AB, then the line AC is contained in the line AB.

XI. If A and B are distinct points, there is at least one point not lying on the line AB.

XII. If A, B, C are non-collinear points, and A' is a point on BC, distinct from B and C, and B' is a point on CA, distinct from C and A, then the lines AA' and BB' possess a point in common.

---

* Cf. *I Principii della Geometria di Posizione*, by M. Pieri, Accad. R. di Torino, 1898.

† Note 'line' here means the complete line and not the segment, which is introduced later. Also 'line' is used in the sequel habitually for 'straight line.'

Definition. If *A, B, C* are three non-collinear points, the plane *ABC* is the class of points lying on the lines joining *A* to the various points on *BC*.

Axioms I to XI hold in any geometry, projective or descriptive, according to the definition of the subject; but in descriptive geometry they would be very inconvenient as axioms. Axiom XII is characteristic of projective geometry. The definition replaces the definition of a plane given in § 3. It will be noticed that if this definition were applied to Euclidean Geometry, which is descriptive, the line through *A* parallel to *BC* would be omitted from the plane *ABC*.

It can now be proved that any two distinct points in a line determine the line, and that any three non-collinear points in a plane determine the plane; also that a line joining two points in a plane lies wholly in the plane, and that any two lines in a plane intersect.

5. The definition of harmonic conjugates, which is the turning point of the whole subject, can now be introduced. The definition* is as follows : *D* is the harmonic conjugate of *B* with respect to *A* and *C*, if the four points are collinear, and if a complete quadrangle can be found such that one pair of opposite sides intersect at *A*, another pair of opposite sides at *C*, and the third pair of opposite sides pass respectively through *B* and *D*.

The notation, Harm (*ABCD*), will be used to mean, *D* is the harmonic conjugate of *B* with respect to *A* and *C*.

It can easily be proved that Harm (*ABCD*) implies Harm (*ADCB*) and Harm (*CBAD*), also that, if *A, B, C* be any three distinct collinear points, there is a point *D* such that Harm (*ABCD*), and that in this case *D* will be distinct from *A* and *C*.

But three other essential theorems respecting harmonic conjugates cannot be established without further axioms. The first theorem is, that Harm (*ABCD*) and Harm (*ABCD'*) imply the identity of *D* and *D'*; the second theorem is, that Harm (*ABCD*) implies Harm (*BCDA*); and the third theorem is, that Harm (*ABCD*) implies the diversity of *B* and *D*.

6. Let *FGHK* be a quadrangle such that *FG* and *HK* pass through *A*, *FK* and *GH* through *C*, *GK* through *B*, and *FH* through *D* (cf. annexed figure).

---

* Cf. v. Staudt, *Geometrie der Lage*, § 8, paragraph 93.

Let $F'G'H'K'$ be another quadrangle (not shown in the figure) with the same property except that FH passes through D' on AC. Firstly let $F'G'H'K'$ be not coplanar with $FGHK$, then evidently any pair of the lines FF', GG', KK' intersect, and so do any pair of GG', HH', KK'. Also no three of these lines are coplanar. Hence they intersect in the same point. Hence FH and $F'H'$ are coplanar, and D and D' must each be the point in which ABC intersects this plane. Thus D

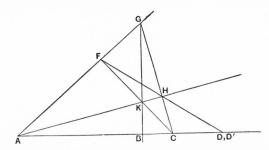

and D' coincide. Secondly let the two quadrangles be coplanar. Then considering the triangles FGK and $F'G'K'$, the pairs of homologously named sides intersect in the collinear points A, B, C. Hence, if we assume Desargues' Theorem respecting coaxial and perspective triangles, FF', GG', KK' are concurrent. Similarly GG', HH' and KK' are concurrent. Hence in the triangles FGH and $F'G'H'$, we have FF', GG', HH' concurrent.

Thus again using Desargues' Theorems, the pairs of homologously named sides intersect in three collinear points. But A and C are two of these points. Hence D and D' coincide.

Thus the proof of the required theorem depends on Desargues' Theorems of Perspective Triangles.

Again the proof* that Harm $(ABCD)$ implies Harm $(BCDA)$ also requires Desargues' Perspective Theorems. Also it requires the theorem that B and D are distinct points. For (cf. annexed figure) let the quadrangle $EFGH$ be such that EF and GH are concurrent in A, and EH and FG in C, and FH and EG pass respectively through D and B. Let FH and EG intersect in K. Then (assuming that D and B are distinct points) the triangles EFC and DBK are coaxial, and hence by Desargues' Theorem ED, FB, and CK are concurrent, say in the point L. Then the quadrangle $EKFL$ has sides LE and FK concurrent in D, sides LF and EK concurrent in B, the side LK

* Cf. v. Staudt, *G. d. L.* § 8, paragraph 96.

through C, and the side EF through A. Hence we find Harm $(BCDA)$.

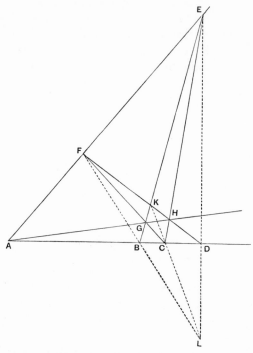

7. To prove Desargues' Theorems, first let the two coplanar triangles ABC, $A'B'C'$ be in perspective, so that AA', BB', CC' are

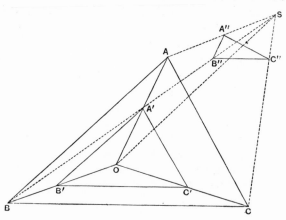

concurrent in O. Assuming that the space is at least of three dimensions, take any point S outside the plane, and join SA, SB, SC. Then the planes SOA, SOB, and SOC have a common line of intersection SO. But in the line SO there are at least three points, and thus there is on it a point S' distinct from S and O. Let $S'A'$ and SA intersect in A'', $S'B'$ and SB in B'', $S'C'$ and SC in C''. Let l be the line of intersection of the plane $A''B''C''$ with the plane ABC. Then BC and $B''C''$ intersect on l, and so do $B'C'$ and $B''C''$. Hence BC and $B'C'$ intersect on l, and similarly for the other sides. Thus perspective triangles are coaxial.

Secondly, let the two coplanar triangles ABC, $A'B'C'$ be coaxial, so that BC and $B'C'$ intersect on the line l, and similarly for CA and $C'A'$, and for AB and $A'B'$. Then by hypothesis a point A'' exists outside the plane, and a point S, distinct from A and A'', exists on the line AA''. Let SB and SC intersect the plane $A''l$ in B'' and C''. Then BC, $B'C'$, $B''C''$ intersect on l, hence $B'B''$ and $C'C''$ are concurrent. Thus the three lines $A'A''$, $B'B''$, $C'C''$ are concurrent in some point S'. Hence the three planes $AA'A''$, $BB'B''$, $CC'C''$ have the common line of intersection SS', which meets the plane ABC in some point O. Then AA', BB', CC' are concurrent in O.

Accordingly Desargues' Theorems can be proved, if three (or more) dimensions are assumed in addition to the preceding axioms.

The requisite axiom can be worded* thus :

XIII. If A, B, C are any three non-collinear points, there exists at least one point external to the plane ABC.

Peano†, and subsequently Hilbert‡, have proved that, if the Geometry be two dimensional, that is, if axiom XIII be excluded, the preceding axioms together with the contradictory of Desargues' Theorem form a consistent system.

For consider plane Euclidean Geometry, made projective by the addition of the line at infinity, and a set of Cartesian axes, Ox and Oy.

Consider all loci of the form

$$ny = f(y, m/n)\, m\, (x - a),$$

---

* Cf. Pieri, *loc. cit.*

† Cf. *Sui fondamenti della Geometria*, Rivista di Matematica, vol. IV. 1894, p. 73.

‡ Cf. *Grundlagen der Geometrie*, 1899. A simplified form of Hilbert's proof is given by K. Th. Vahlen, *Abstrakte Geometrie*, Leipzig, 1905, p. 68. The proof in the text, which is much simpler than any of those above mentioned, was given by R. F. Moulton, *A simple non-desarguesian Plane Geometry*, Trans. Amer. Math. Soc., vol III. 1902.

where m, n, and a are variable parameters, each set of values characterizing one member of the family of loci, and $f(y, m/n)$ is the same function for all members of the family, defined as follows :

If $\quad\quad\quad\quad m/n \leqq 0$, then $f(y, m/n) = 1$,

if $\quad\quad\quad\quad m/n > 0, \; y \leqq 0$, then $f(y, m/n) = 1$,

if $\quad\quad\quad\quad m/n > 0, \; y > 0$, then $f(y, m/n) = c$,

where c has some definite fixed positive value, not unity.

Call the loci of this family 'modified lines,' and include in the family the line at infinity. Then a modified line consists of two parts, portions of two straight lines, like the line A_1KM in the annexed

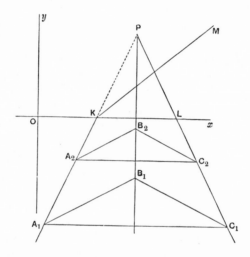

figure, or else, if $m/n \leqq 0$, it is an ordinary straight line, for instance PC_1 in the figure. A modified line may be considered as refracted at the axis of x, when m/n is positive.

Solving the equations

$$ny = m(x - a), \text{ and } n_1 y = m_1 (x - a_1),$$

we find $\quad\quad\quad\quad y = mm_1 (a_1 - a)/(nm_1 - n_1 m) \; ;$

and solving the equations

$$ny' = cm(x' - a), \text{ and } n_1 y' = cm_1 (x' - a_1),$$

we find $\quad\quad\quad\quad y' = cmm_1 (a_1 - a)/(nm_1 - n_1 m).$

Thus y and y' are either both positive, or both negative, or both zero. Accordingly one and only one modified line joins any two points. It can therefore be easily seen that taking the points of the Euclidean plane to be the points of axioms I—XII, and the modified lines to be the lines of these axioms, then the axioms are all satisfied.

But Desargues' theorem of perspective triangles is not satisfied with this determination of points and lines. For notice that if the parts of two modified lines below the axis of x $(y < 0)$ are parallel, the parts above the axis of x are also parallel. Now (cf. annexed figure) let $A_1B_1C_1$ and $A_2B_2C_2$ be two triangles, both below the axis of x, and with their homologous sides parallel ; also let the triangles be so placed that PC_2C_1, PB_2B_1, MKA_2A_1 are the modified lines through C_1 and C_2, B_1 and B_2, A_1 and A_2. Then evidently Desargues' Theorem is not satisfied.

8. The theorem, that Harm $(ABCD)$ implies the diversity of B and D, has been shown by Fano* not to follow from the preceding axioms. This is proved by the consideration of a three dimensional geometry in which there are only fifteen points. Since we are only concerned with a finite number of entities, we can form our classes, such as straight lines and planes, by mere enumeration of their members. To facilitate this enumeration, choose any five of the entities and name them a, b, c, d, e. Call these the simply-named entities. The remaining ten entities are named (ab), (ac), ... (de) ; these are the doubly-named entities. Thus the fifteen points are all named, and divided by their names into two types. Note that the names (ab) and (ba) are not distinguished. Every straight line contains three and only three points, and the relations between the names of the points divide them into three types. TYPE I consists of all classes such as the class composed of a, b and (ab) ; there are ten examples of this type. TYPE II consists of all classes such as the class composed of (bc), (ac), (ab) ; there are ten examples of this type. TYPE III consists of all classes such as the class composed of a, (bc), (de) ; there are fifteen examples of this type. Thus there are in all 35 straight lines in this space. For example, d, e and (de) compose a line of the first type, and (bc), (cd) and (bd) compose a line of the second type, and e, (bc), (ad) compose a line of the third type.

Any set of three points not of one of these types defines a plane. There are ten types of sets of three non-collinear points, which may be defined by examples thus :

* *Sui postulati fondamentali della Geometria projettiva*, Giorn. di Matemat., vol. xxx. 1891; also cf. Pieri, *loc. cit.*

Type I by a, b, c; Type II by $a, b, (ac)$;

Type III by $a, b, (cd)$; Type IV by $a, (ab), (ac)$;

Type V by $a, (ab), (bc)$; Type VI by $a, (ab), (cd)$;

Type VII by $(ab), (ac), (de)$; Type VIII by $a, (bc), (bd)$;

Type IX by $(ab), (ac), (ad)$; Type X by $(ab), (ac), (bd)$.

There are two types of planes, each plane containing seven points and seven straight lines. Type I contains non-collinear triple sets from Type I to Type VII inclusive; while Type II of planes contains non-collinear triple sets of Types VIII, IX and X. The annexed figures illustrate the types of planes.

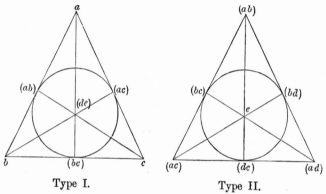

Type I. Type II.

In these figures the named points on straight lines are points on straight lines in the finite geometry, also the named points of contact of the circles are collinear in the finite geometry. Now in the example of Type I, (bc) is its own harmonic conjugate with respect to b and c; and in the example of Type II, (dc) is its own harmonic conjugate with respect to (ac) and (ad).

It is evident that the projective axioms hitherto given are all satisfied. Also the Geometry is three dimensional. For there are seven points on any given plane: take a point outside the plane, and join it with each of the seven points; there is one remaining point on each of these lines. Accordingly all the fifteen points are thus used up.

Hence an axiom, which we may call 'Fano's axiom,' is required.

XIV. If Harm $(ABCD)$ holds, then B and D are diverse points.

An equivalent form* of this axiom is, the three harmonic points of

* Cf. Pieri, *Nuovi Principii di Geometria Projettiva Complessa*, Trans. Accad. R. di Torino, 1905. Note that subsequent references to Pieri refer to the other memoir previously mentioned.

a complete quadrilateral are not collinear. The equivalence of the two forms of the axiom is obvious from a figure.

The axiom which limits the Geometry to three dimensions will now be given. It is not stated by Pieri, who never requires it in his reasonings. It will be wanted here when we come to the introduction of coordinates.

XV. There exists a plane a and a point A, not incident in a, such that any point lies in some line possessing A and some point of a.

Note that this axiom is not true for Euclidean space. For the plane through A, parallel to a, would be omitted. The property is enunciated for one plane and one point. It can then be shown to hold for every plane and every point external to it. Also it can be proved that any two planes intersect in a straight line.

CHAPTER III

PROJECTIVITY

9. (a) When two figures can be derived one from the other by a single projection, they are said to be 'in perspective'; when two figures can be derived one from the other by a finite series of perspective transformations, they are said to be 'projectively' related. A property of a figure, which is necessarily also possessed by any figure projective with it, is called a 'projective property.' The symbol

$$(ABC...) \overline{\wedge} (A'B'C'...)$$

will mean that the range $ABC...$ is projective with the range $A'B'C'...$, A corresponding to A', etc. If a series of n perspective transformations exists which finally transform the range $ABC...$ into the range $A'B'C'...$, the figures will be said to have a 'projective relation of the nth degree,' and the fact will be expressed by $(ABC...) \overline{\wedge}_n (A'B'C'...)$. Thus $(ABC...) \overline{\wedge}_n (A'B'C'...)$ implies $(ABC...) \overline{\wedge} (A'B'C'...)$; and also $(ABC...) \overline{\wedge}_1 (A'B'C'...)$ expresses that the ranges $ABC...$ and $A'B'C'...$ are perspectively related. Also if the vertex $(U,$ say$)$ of a perspectivity is to be expressed, $\overline{\wedge}_1$ will be replaced by $\overline{\wedge}_U$.

(β) The above is not v. Staudt's definition* of projectivity. According to his definition, the points on two lines (which may be identical) are projectively related when there is a one-one correspondence between them, such that if A, B, C, D are any four points on one line, and A', B', C', D' are their correspondents on the other line, then Harm $(ABCD)$ and Harm $(A'B'C'D')$ imply each other. Let us call such a correspondence a 'Harmonically Projective' relation between the lines.

(γ) There are now two propositions to be considered. One of them is the proposition that a projective correspondence between two

---

* Cf. *G. d. L.* § 9, paragraph 103.

lines is completely determined when the correspondents of three distinct points on one line are determined on the other. This proposition has earned itself the title of 'The fundamental proposition of Projective Geometry.' The other proposition is, that a harmonically projective correspondence between two lines is a projective correspondence. It will be found that these propositions cannot be proved without further axioms.

(δ) Since the quadrilateral construction is projective, it is easily seen that it follows from our axioms that, if A, B, C, D satisfy Harm $(ABCD)$, the property is projective. Hence it immediately follows that a projective correspondence between the points on two lines is a harmonically projective correspondence.

10. If the axes* of the ranges $ABC...$ and $A'B'C'...$ are distinct, and if n is greater than 1, then $(ABC...) \overline{\wedge}_n (A'B'C'...)$ implies $(ABC...) \overline{\wedge}_2 (A'B'C'...)$†. The proof of this theorem requires two lemmas.

Lemma I. If $(ABCD...) \overline{\wedge}_1 (AB''C''D''...)$,

and $(AB''C''D''...) \overline{\wedge}_1 (AB'C'D'...)$,

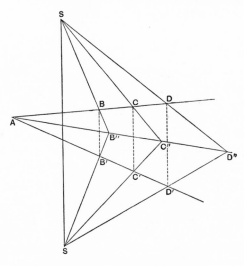

then $(ABCD...) \overline{\wedge}_1 (AB'C'D'...)$.

---

* The axis of a range of points is the straight line which possesses them all.

† Cf. F. Schur, *Ueber den Fundamentalsatz der projectiven Geometrie*, Math. Annal. vol. LI. 1899.

For (cf. annexed fig.) let S and S' be the centres of the two per-spectivities, and let BB' intersect SS' in S_1 (not shown in figure). Then by Desargues' Theorem, since $BB'B''$ and $CC'C'''$ are in per-spective, the intersection of BB' and CC' must be on SS', and hence CC'' passes through S_1. Similarly for DD', and so on.

Lemma II. A relation of projectivity of the 2nd degree between the lines g_1 and g_3, namely two perspectivities from g_1 to g_2 and from g_2 to g_3 respectively, can be modified by replacing g_2 by any line not passing through the point (g_1g_3), and not joining corresponding points of g_1 and g_3*.

Let S_1 (cf. annexed figure) be the centre of perspectivity from g_1 to g_2, and S_2 that from g_2 to g_3. Let LM be the line which is to replace

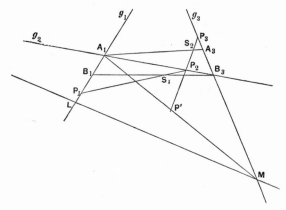

g_2, where by hypothesis L and M are distinct, and L does not correspond to M. Let A_1 be (g_1g_2) and B_3 be (g_2g_3). Then

$$(P_1\ldots)\ \overline{\wedge}_1(P_2\ldots)\ \overline{\wedge}_1(P_3\ldots).$$

Firstly, assume that M is not A_3. Project $[P_3\ldots]$ from S_2 on to A_1M, producing $[P'\ldots]$. Then by Lemma I, $(P_1\ldots)\ \overline{\wedge}_1(P'\ldots)$. Hence g_2 has been replaced by A_1M. Now in exactly the same way, since L and M do not correspond, by interchanging the roles of g_1 and g_3, A_1M can be replaced by LM. Secondly, if M coincides with A_3, by the first case replace g_2 by $L'M'$, where L' is distinct from A_1 and M' from A_3; and then, again by the first case, replace $L'M'$ by LM.

* I am indebted to Professor Veblen of Princeton for the following proof, which differs from Schur's. It was given by him in lectures (*On the Foundations of Geometry*) in the University of Chicago, 1905. Mimeographed copies of the notes exist. I have found them to be most instructive.

The main theorem can now be proved. Let there be a perspective relation from g_1 to g_2, from g_2 to g_3, and from g_3 to g_4. Through the point (g_3, g_4) draw any line h, so that (h, g_1) does not correspond

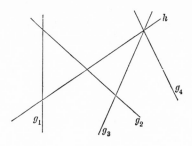

to (g_3, g_4) on g_3. Then by Lemma II, there are perspective relations from g_1 to h and from h to g_3, which give the same correspondents on g_3. Also by Lemma I the resulting projective relation of the 2nd degree between h and g_4 can be replaced by a perspective relation. Hence the projective relation of the 3rd degree between g_1 and g_4 can be replaced by one of the 2nd degree. Hence in a series of n perspective transformations, sequences of three can continually be replaced by sequences of two such transformations, either as above, or, in exceptional cases (when g_1, g_2, g_3, g_4 are not all distinct) by a use of Lemma I, as it is easy to see.

11. The proof of the 'Fundamental Theorem' can be reduced to depend on Desargues' perspective theorem, and on Pascal's theorem for the case when the conic is two straight lines (Pappus' Theorem)*.

Let A, B, C on the line g correspond to A_1, B_1, C_1 on the line g_1. By § 10, the projective relation can be reduced to one of the 2nd degree, and by Lemma II of § 10 the intervening line can be chosen to join any two non-corresponding points of g and g_1. Let it join A and B_1; call AB_1 the line g'. Then (to obtain a projective relation with the required properties) the centre of the perspectivity between g and g' can be chosen to be the point $(BB_1 . CC_1)$, say S; and the centre of that between g' and g_1 must then be the point $(AA_1 . CC_1)$, say S_1. By this projective relation P corresponds to P_1, by the intermediary of P' on g'. Now if by any other projective relation P corresponds to P_1'

---

* This was pointed out without proof by H. Wiener, cf. *Jahresbericht der Deutschen Math. Ver.* vol. 1, 1890. The proof here given is due to Schur, *loc. cit.*

on g_1, project P_1' on to g' from S_1 into the point P''. Then $(ABCP)$ is projective with $(AB_1C'P'')$.

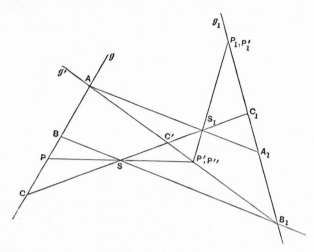

Hence if we can prove that these ranges, with the self-corresponding point A, are in perspective, then BB_1, CC', PP'' are concurrent; and thence P', P'', and P_1, P_1' coincide.

To prove that two projective ranges (on lines g and g') with a self-

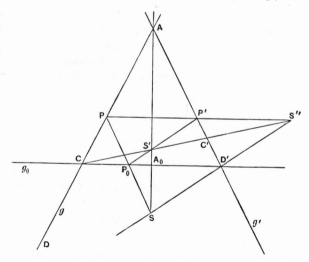

corresponding point are in perspective, reduce by § 10 the projectivity to the 2nd degree, with g_0 as the intervening line, and S, S' as the centres of perspective. Then since the point (g, g') is self-corresponding, either g_0 or SS' passes through (g, g'). In the first case, the theorem follows from Lemma I of § 10. In the second case let g_0 cut g and g' in C and D', and let A be (g, g'), and P, P_0, P' a variable trio of correspondents on g, g_0, g' respectively. Then on the two lines CD' and ASS', consider the hexagon $CS'P_0SD'A$; by Pascal's Theorem for two lines the three points (CS', SD'), $(S'P_0, D'A)$, (P_0S, AC) are collinear; that is, the points P, P', S'' are collinear, where S'' is the point (CS', SD'). Hence the projective ranges $[P]$ and $[P']$ are in perspective. Conversely, if the fundamental theorem is assumed, Pappus' Theorem holds. For the proof will be the well-known projective proof of Pascal's theorem adapted to the case when the conic is two straight lines.

12.　The establishment of the Pappus Theorem can be investigated as follows*.

Let two straight lines, intersecting in O, contain respectively the two trios of points E_1, E_3, E_5, and E_2, E_4, E_6, all distinct and distinct from O. Assuming three dimensions at least, there is a point, (12) say, not in the plane OE_1E_2. Also on the line E_2 (12), there is at least one other point, (23) say, distinct from E_2 and (12). Now the plane E_4E_1 (12) intersects the line E_3 (23) in the single point (34), say. Hence the line E_4 (34) intersects the coplanar line E_1(12) in the point (14). Similarly from E_6 the single line E_6 (16) (26) can be drawn intersecting E_1 (12) and E_3 (23) in (16) and (26). Also similarly from E_5 the single line E_5 (54) (25) can be drawn intersecting E_2 (12) and E_4 (14) in the points (25) and (54). If now we may assume that E_5 (25) and E_6 (16) intersect in (56), we may proceed as follows. Let D be the point $(E_1E_2 . E_4E_5)$, E the point $(E_2E_3 . E_5E_6)$, F the point $(E_3E_4 . E_6E_1)$, also let π be the plane OE_1E_2. Also mention the other planes by *all* the marked points on them.

Thus D lies in the planes

$$\pi, \quad \{E_1E_2(12)\ (14)\ (16)\ (23)\ (25)\}, \quad \{E_4E_5\ (14)\ (34)\ (54)\ (25)\}.$$

Thus D is the intersection of the line (14) (25) with π.

Again E is the intersection of the planes

$$\pi, \quad \{E_5E_6(16)\ (36)\}, \quad \{E_5E_6(45)\ (25)\}, \quad \{E_2E_3(12)\ (23)\ (25)\ (43)\ (36)\}.$$

---

* Cf. Schur, *loc. cit.*, who refers this proof to Dandelin, *Recherches nouvelles*, *etc.*, Annales de Gergonne, vol. xv.

But, from the assumption as to the existence of (56), the planes
$$\{E_5 E_6 (16)\,(36)\} \quad \text{and} \quad \{E_5 E_6 (45)\,(25)\}$$
form the single plane
$$\{E_5 E_6 (16)\,(36)\,(45)\,(25)\}.$$
Thus E is the intersection of the line (25) (36) with π.

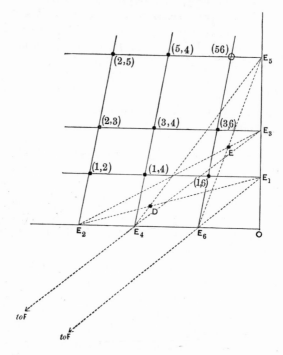

Again F is the intersection of the planes
$$\pi, \quad \{E_3 E_4 (36)\,(34)\,(23)\,(14)\,(54)\}, \quad \{E_1 E_6 (16)\,(14)\,(12)\,(36)\}.$$
Thus F is the intersection of the line (14) (36) with π.
Accordingly D, E, F all lie in the line
$$\{\pi \,.\, (14)\,(25)\,(36)\}.$$
Thus the Pappus Theorem is established.

Conversely, if Pappus' Theorem is assumed, the existence of the point (56) can be proved. For now D, E, and F are collinear ; also D and F lie in the line $\{\pi \,.\, (14)\,(25)\,(36)\}$. Then since E lies in DF, it is the intersection of the three planes
$$\pi, \quad \{(14)\,(25)\,(36)\}, \quad \{E_2 E_3 (12)\,(23)\,(25)\,(43)\,(36)\} ;$$

(δ) If P, Q, R, S respectively stand among other terms in this relation in any order with the same pair of terms A and B, then either

$S(PQRS)$, or $S(PRQS)$, or $S(PRSQ)$,

(ε) If $S(ABCD)$ and $S(ACBE)$,

then $S(ADBE)$.

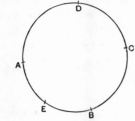

The relation of separation, S, as defined above, can be proved to satisfy these conditions.

15. A relation among the points on a line can be defined which arranges them in an open order, with any arbitrarily assumed point A, of the line as the initial point.

If A, B, C are three distinct collinear points, then E is said to follow D in the S-order (ABC), if any of the following cases hold:

(1)　D lies in segm (ABC) and E in segm (ACD) ;

(2)　D lies in segm $(A\hat{B}C)$, excluding A and C, and E lies in segm $(A\hat{C}D)$, excluding A and D ;

(3)　D coincides with A, and E is any other point of the line ;

(4)　D coincides with C, and E lies in segm $(A\hat{B}C)$, excluding A and C.

It can be proved that if A, B, C are distinct and collinear points, and E follows D in the S-order (ABC), and D is distinct from A, then the S-orders (ABC) and (ADE) are the same for any two points of the line.

The S-order (ABC) is said to be 'concordant' with the S-order (DEF)—expressed symbolically by (ABC) S-concord (DEF)—when either of the three following cases hold : In the S-order (ABC), *either* (1) E follows D, E follows F, and D follows F, *or* (2) E follows D, F follows E, and F follows D, *or* (3) D follows E, F follows E, and D follows F. In the other three possible cases with respect to the order of D, E, F on the line ABC, the S-orders (ABC) and (DEF) are said to be discordant—expressed symbolically by (ABC) S-discord (DEF).

Then it can be proved that if A, B, C are three distinct collinear points, and D, E, F are three distinct points on the line ABC, the S-order (DEF) is concordant with one and only one of the S-orders (ABC) and (ACB), and also that the S-orders (ABC) and (BCA) are concordant.

and hence E is the point of intersection of the line $(25)(36)$ with π. But E also lies in the intersection of

$$\pi,\quad \{E_5E_6(16)(36)\},\quad \{E_5E_6(45)(25)\}.$$

Thus the line $(25)(36)$ must intersect E_5E_6. Hence the two planes

$$\{E_5E_6(16)(36)\}\ \text{and}\ \{E_5E_6(25)(45)\}$$

are identical ; and hence the point (56) exists.

The assumption [as to the existence of (56)] made in the course of the proof of Pappus' Theorem has not been deduced from the preceding axioms. Hilbert* has shown that Pappus' Theorem cannot be deduced from axioms I to XV. Thus the 'fundamental theorem,' or some equivalent theorem, must be assumed as an axiom.

But there is an entirely different line of proof (requiring further axioms) of the fundamental theorem, which may be called 'von Staudt's† continuity proof.'

This proof in its original form contains an oversight, which was first pointed out by Klein‡. The proof will be given here in its amended form. The proof requires that relations of order among points on lines should have been introduced.

Furthermore for the case of Geometries with a finite number of points, it has been shown by J. H. Maclagan-Wedderburn§ that Pappus' Theorem can be proved without any further axioms, beyond the aforesaid one of finiteness of number.

---

* Cf. *loc. cit.*, chapter VI, and §§ 44 to 48 of this tract.

† Cf. *Geometrie der Lage*, § 9, paragraph 106.

‡ Cf. *Zweiten Aufsatze über nicht-Euclidische Geometrie*, Math. Annal. vol. VI. 1873.

§ Cf. *A Theorem on finite Algebras*, Trans. Amer. Math. Soc. vol. VI. 1905, and *Finite Projective Geometries*, by O. Veblen and W. H. Bussey, Trans. Amer. Math. Soc. vol. VII. 1906, p. 246.

CHAPTER IV

ORDER

13. If A, B, C are three collinear points, the segment ABC—written segm (ABC)—is defined* to be the collection of all collinear points X, such that there is some pair of points y and y' satisfying both Harm $(AyCy')$ and Harm $(ByXy')$. Also segm $(A\hat{B}C)$ is the collection of all points on the line ABC which do not lie on segm (ABC). The extreme instances of the various definitions are so arranged that A and C do not belong to segm (ABC), and that B does belong to segm (ABC).

The basis of these definitions can easily be perceived by considering the Euclidean line made projective by adding in the point at infinity. For if B on such a line lies between A and C, and X is any other point

between A and C, then, since pairs of harmonic conjugates separate each other, the two point-pairs A, C and B, X define an involution with real double points, say y and y'. Thus in the Euclidean line, if X be any point in the segment AC in which B also lies, the two points y and y' exist with the property described in the above definition of segm (ABC). Conversely this characteristic property is here taken as the definition.

It can be proved without any further axioms that the propositions, D belongs to segm (ABC), and, B belongs to segm (ADC), imply each other. Also if D lies in segm (ABC) and is distinct from B, then C

* Cf. Pieri, *loc. cit.*

lies in segm (BAD). Also if D lies in segm $(A\hat{B}C)$ and is distinct from A, then C lies in segm $(B\hat{A}D)$.

Furthermore since the harmonic property of four points is projective, it follows that both the properties expressed by D belongs to segm (ABC), and D belongs to segm $(A\hat{B}C)$, are projective.

14. But further axioms are required to complete the usual properties of segments. They can be enunciated (cf. Pieri, *loc. cit.*) as follows :

XVI. If A, B, C are three distinct collinear points, and D is distinct from A and C, and belongs to segm $(A\hat{B}C)$, then D belongs to segm (BCA).

XVII. If A, B, C are three distinct collinear points, and D belongs both to segm (BCA) and to segm (CAB), it cannot belong to segm (ABC).

XVIII. If A, B, C are three distinct collinear points, and D is a point, distinct from B, belonging to segm (ABC), then segm (ADC) is contained in segm (ABC).

The above are the three axioms of order. A relation of separation to hold between two couples, A and C, B and D, of collinear points can be defined thus : A and C will be said to 'separate' B and D, which will be expressed symbolically by $S(ABCD)$—when A, B, C are four distinct collinear points, and D belongs to segm $(A\hat{B}C)$.

The conditions which must be satisfied by such a relation of separation (S), so that it may arrange the points on each line in closed order have been investigated by Vailati*. These conditions as follows :

(α) $S(ABCD)$ is equivalent to $S(BADC)$,
(β) $S(ABCD)$ is equivalent to $S(ADCB)$,
(γ) $S(ABCD)$ excludes $S(ACBD)$,

* Cf. two papers in vol. v. of the Rivista di Matematica (Turin), 18 *relazioni di posizione tra punti d' una linea chiusa*, and, *Sulle proprietà cara delle varietà a una dimensione.* The whole question of order is ex considered by Russell, *Principles of Mathematics*, ch. XXIV and XXV

We thus arrive at the idea of a 'sense' (or, way) round a line*; if A, B, C are three distinct collinear points, and D, P, Q are three distinct points on this line, and by some process of correspondence P is related to Q, then, if (DPQ) δ-concord (ABC), P will be said to move to Q by this correspondence in the sense (ABC) from D.

Discordant senses (ABC) and (CBA) are also said to be 'opposed.' Concordant senses are called the same sense.

16. If A, B, C be three distinct collinear points, the two segments segm (ABC) and segm $(A\hat{B}C)$ are called the 'segments between A and C,' and they are said to be complementary to each other.

Segments, as defined above, possess, *either* two terminal points— such as A and C in segm $(A\hat{B}C)$,—*or* two bounding points belonging to the complementary segment—such as A and C bounding segm (ABC). The definition of a segment will now be enlarged so that this property of being 'between' two points does not flow from the definition.

A segment of a line is now defined to be a set of points on the line, (1) which does not include the whole line, (2) which includes at least two distinct points on the line, (3) which is such that, if A and B be any two distinct points belonging to it, one of the two complementary segments between A and B is contained entirely within it.

Thus, when A, B, C are collinear, segm (ABC) and segm $(A\hat{B}C)$ are themselves both segments in this enlarged sense; but, without a further axiom, it cannot be inferred that every segment is 'between' two points.

A set of points on a line is said to be 'compact,' if every segment between two distinct members of the set possesses at least one other member of the set.

A set of points on a line is said to be 'everywhere dense,' if every segment of the line contains at least one member of the set.

A set of points on a line can be compact without being everywhere dense.

17. Since 'D belongs to segm (ABC),' and 'E belongs to segm $(A\hat{B}C)$,' express projective properties of the ranges $ABCD$ and $ABCE$, it follows that $S(ABCD)$ expresses a projective property, and similarly that, 'E follows D in the S-order (ABC),' and, '(ABC) S- $\left\{ \begin{matrix} \text{concord} \\ \text{discord} \end{matrix} \right\}$ (DEF),' express projective properties.

---

* Cf. von Staudt, *Beiträge zur Geometrie der Lage*, § 3, and Pieri, *loc. cit.*

Three important theorems must now be proved.

(a) If A, B, C are distinct, Harm $(ABCD)$ implies $S(ABCD)$.

For since we have Harm $(ABCD)$, points A', B', C', U, V can be found as in the annexed figure.   Then

$$(ABCD) \overline{\wedge}_U (A'B'C'D) \overline{\wedge}_V (CBAD).$$

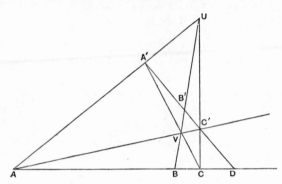

Hence, if $S(ACBD)$ held, it would be projected into $S(CABD)$. But these two relations are inconsistent.   Thus $S(ACBD)$ cannot hold. Similarly $S(ACDB)$ cannot hold.   Therefore $S(ABCD)$ must hold.

(β) Harm $(ABCD)$ and Harm (AB_1CD_1) imply that $S(ABB_1C)$ and $S(ADD_1C)$ are equivalent.

For the conditions Harm $(ABCD)$ and Harm (AB_1CD_1), render the annexed figure possible.   Hence

$$(ABB_1C) \overline{\wedge}_U (A'VV_1C) \overline{\wedge}_A (UC'C_1'C) \overline{\wedge}_{A'} (ADD_1C).$$

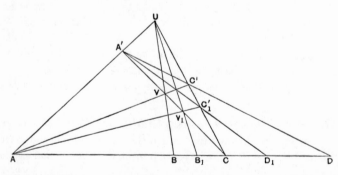

Hence $S(ABB_1C)$ and $S(ADD_1C)$ are equivalent.   This proposition may be loosely expressed by saying that B and D move in opposed senses to or from C.

(γ) Harm $(ABCD)$ and Harm (ABC_1D_1) imply that $S(ABCC_1)$ and $S(ABDD_1)$ are equivalent.

For the conditions Harm $(ABCD)$ and Harm (ABC_1D_1) immediately secure the possibility of the annexed figure, apart from

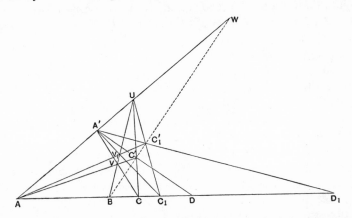

the dotted line. Then in the triangles CVC' and $C_1V_1C_1'$, the point $(CV . C_1V_1)$ is A', the point $(VC' . V_1C_1')$ is A, and the point $(CC' . C_1C_1')$ is U. But A', A, U are collinear. Hence by Desargues' Perspective Theorem, CC_1, VV_1, and $C'C_1'$ are concurrent.

Hence $C'C_1'$ passes through B; let it also cut $AA'U$ in W. Then

$$(ABCC_1) \overline{\wedge}_{A'} (UBVV_1) \overline{\wedge}_A (WBC'C_1') \overline{\wedge}_{A'} (ABDD_1).$$

Hence $S(ABCC_1)$ and $S(ABDD_1)$ are equivalent.

This proposition is loosely expressed by saying that C and D move from A (or B) in the same sense.

18. If A, B, C are three distinct collinear points, the harmonic system (ABC) is the system of points arrived at by the following inductive definition : A, B, C are the initial set of points, A, B, C, D_1, D_2, D_3 are the second set of points, where D_1, D_2, D_3 are respectively the harmonic conjugates of A with respect to B and C, of B with respect to C and A, and of C with respect to A and B, and the $(n+1)$th set is derived from the nth set by adding to the nth set the harmonic conjugates of each point of the nth set with respect to any other two points of the nth set.

It is evident, from the projectivity of the harmonic relation, that a harmonic system projects into a harmonic system. Furthermore since two sets of three distinct collinear points are projective, it follows that any two harmonic systems are projective.

A harmonic system is compact. For, if A and B are any two points of a harmonic system, since any system possesses at least three points, there is a third point D in one of the two segments between A and B. Now take E to satisfy Harm $(ADBE)$, then E lies in segm $(A\hat{D}B)$. Hence there is also another point in the other segment between A and B.

But a compact system possesses necessarily an infinite number of points. Hence every harmonic system, and therefore every straight line, possesses an infinite number of points. Accordingly the axioms of order, given above, and Fano's axiom have excluded the geometries with a finite number of points.

von Staudt in his proof of the fundamental theorem* wrongly assumed that every compact system of collinear points must be everywhere dense. This theorem will now be proved for any harmonic system. It will be called the Lüroth-Zeuthen theorem†. It will be noticed that a fresh axiom is required.

19. (a) The new axiom, which will be referred to as the Dedekind‡ axiom, or as enunciating the Dedekind property, is as follows.

XIX. If u is any segment of a line, there are two points A and B, such that, if P be any member of u distinct from A and B, segm (APB) is all of u with the possible exception of either or both of A and B which may also belong to u.

Note that the axioms of order, viz. XVI, XVII, XVIII, and this axiom need only be enunciated for *one* line. Then by projection they can be proved for every line.

(β) Consider any segment of a line, to prove that at least one point of any given harmonic system of the line must lie within it. Let the segment be enlarged (if possible at either end) to its full extent so long as no fresh point of the harmonic system is included. Now *assume*

---

* Cf. *Geom. der Lage*, § 9, paragraph 103.

† von Staudt's tacit assumption was pointed out by Klein, *Zweiten Aufsatz über nicht-Euclidische Geometrie*, Math. Annal. vol. IV. 1873. The proof here given was communicated to Klein simultaneously by Lüroth and Zeuthen, and published by Klein in a 'Nachtrag' to the previous article, Math. Annal. vol. VII. 1874.

‡ The importance of the property here considered was first emphasized (for the case of real numbers) by Dedekind, *Stetigkeit und irrationale Zahlen*, 1872. Engl. Trnsl. *Essays on the Theory of Numbers*, by Prof. Beman, Chicago, 1901.

that the line possesses the Dedekind-property. Then the enlarged segment is bounded at each end by points, F and G say. If either F or G belongs to the system, it does not belong to the enlarged segment. Also all the points of the system (if any) in the enlarged segment belong to the original segment.

Firstly let F and G both belong to the system. Then there is another point A belonging to the system. Assume that it belongs to the complementary segment. Take D so that Harm $(AFDG)$. Then D belongs to the enlarged segment and to the harmonic system. Hence it belongs to the original segment and the harmonic system.

Secondly let F and G neither belong to the harmonic system. Hence any segments, abutting on F or G and contained in the

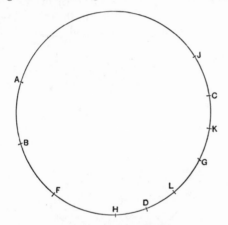

complementary segment, must contain points of the harmonic system. Let A be a point of the system in the complementary segment.

Take H, so that Harm $(AFHG)$ (1).

Take J, so that Harm $(AFGJ)$ (2).

Then (cf. § 17 a) H lies in segm $(F\hat{A}G)$, and J in segm $(A\hat{F}G)$. Now in segm $(A\hat{G}F)$ there is at least one point of the system. Let B be such a point.

Take K, so that Harm $(ABHK)$ (3).

Then by comparing (1) and (3), (cf. § 17 β) as F moves to B, G moves in the opposite sense to K. Also by hypothesis a series of points such as B can be found running in sense (AFG) up to F as a limit. Hence (cf. § 17 a) from (1) the corresponding points K run in sense $(A\hat{F}G)$ up to G as a limit. Hence if C be any point in segm $(G\hat{A}J)$, B and K

may be supposed chosen so that K lies in segm $(G\hat{A}C)$. But at least one point of the system lies in segm $(G\hat{A}J)$; let C be such a point.

Take L, so that Harm $(ABLJ)$ (4).

Take D, so that Harm $(ABDC)$ (5).

Then (cf. § 17 γ) D is in segm $(B\hat{A}C)$; and as J moves to C in sense (GFA), L moves to D in the same sense. Hence D is in segm $(B\hat{A}L)$. But by comparison between (3) and (5), we have (cf. § 17 γ), as C moves to K in sense (GFA) D moves to H in the same sense. Hence D lies in segm $(H\hat{A}C)$. Thus D lies in the common part of segm $(B\hat{A}L)$ and segm $(H\hat{A}C)$, that is, in segm $(H\hat{A}L)$. But this segment is contained in segm $(F\hat{A}G)$. Thus D is a member of the system, and lies in the enlarged segment. Hence it lies in the original segment.

Thirdly let one and only one of F and G—say F—belong to the system.

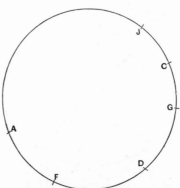

Take A as before in the second case; also take J so that

$$\text{Harm } (AFGJ) \quad (1).$$

Then in segm $(G\hat{F}J)$, a point C belonging to the system exists. Take D so that   Harm $(AFDC)$ (2).

Then J lies as before in the second case. Also (cf. § 17 a) from (2), D lies in segm $(F\hat{A}C)$ and is distinct from F. Again (cf. § 17 γ) by comparing (1) and (2), as J moves to C in sense (GFA), G moves to D in the same sense. Hence D lies in segm $(F\hat{A}G)$, and is distinct from G. Thus a point of the system lies in the enlarged segment, and hence in the original segment.

Accordingly from the three cases it follows that a harmonic system is everywhere dense on the line containing it. But in the proof the Dedekind property is assumed as an axiom.

20. von Staudt's 'continuity proof' of the fundamental theorem (cf. § 10) can now be completed. For consider any projective relation which correlates A, B, C of one line with A', B', C' of another line. Then by the projectivity of the harmonic property, the harmonic system (ABC) is correlated in a determinate manner with the harmonic system $(A'B'C')$. But relations of order are projective. Also any point on the first line not belonging to the harmonic system (ABC) is (cf. § 19) the limit of a class of points belonging to the system. Thus its correlate on the other line must be the limit of the correlated class of points of the other harmonic system. Thus the correlates of all the other points on the two lines are definitely determined.

Hence the fundamental theorem can be proved by the aid of the axioms of order and the axiom of the Dedekind property. Then (cf. § 11) Pappus' Theorem can be deduced.

Maclagan-Wedderburn's Theorem (cf. § 12) proves that the fundamental theorem holds for Geometries with a finite number of points, and the above 'continuity proof' shews that it holds for a Geometry with an infinite number of points in which the above axioms of order and the Dedekind property hold.

We will note in the subsequent work wherever a step in the reasoning depends upon the fundamental theorem or upon the Dedekind property.

We can now prove that a harmonically projective correspondence (cf. § 9) is a projective correspondence. For, since a harmonic system is everywhere dense, a harmonically projective correspondence is completely determined when the correspondents of three points on one of the lines are determined. But it has been proved that there is one and only one projective correspondence which correlates these three points to their assigned correspondents ; and furthermore (cf. § 9) every projective correspondence is a harmonically projective correspondence. Hence the proposition follows.

CHAPTER V

QUADRANGULAR INVOLUTIONS

21. We have now to discuss the dependence of the theory of Involutions upon the Fundamental Theorem. Here the axioms of order, namely XVI, XVII, and XVIII, will not be required till § 32. The projective definition of an involution, as a projective transformation of a line into itself by which each point is interchanged with its correspondent point, at once leads us into difficulties. For the essential theorem on which all depends is that, if in a projective transformation two distinct points are interchanged, the transformation is an involution*.

For consider a projective transformation which interchanges A and B, and transforms C into D. Now (cf. figure) $(ABCD) \overline{\wedge}_S (TUVD)$ $\overline{\wedge}_A (SWVC) \overline{\wedge}_U (BADC)$. Thus there is always at least one projective

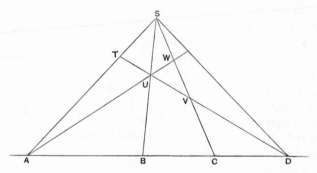

transformation which interchanges A and B, and also C and D. But by the fundamental theorem, there is only one transformation which interchanges A and B, and transforms C into D. Hence this transformation

* Cf. Schur, *Ueber die Grundlagen der Geometrie*, Math. Annal. vol. LV. 1902.

must also transform D into C. But this conclusion does not follow without the fundamental theorem.

Again the general proposition concerning the involutory property of a transversal section of a complete quadrangle does not follow without the fundamental theorem. We can however, without the fundamental theorem, prove the following propositions : If a transversal cuts the three pairs of opposite sides of a complete quadrangle in A and A', B and B', C and C' then

$$(AA'BB'C) \barwedge (A'AB'BC'),$$

with two similar propositions. But it does not follow without the fundamental theorem that the three projective transformations, indicated in the three propositions, are identical.

22. The important property for our present purposes is that of three collinear point-pairs, A and A', B and B', C and C', through which the pairs of opposite sides of a complete quadrangle pass. There is also a further property of such point-pairs, in reference to a quadrangle with the required property, which it is essential to consider. Thus in the annexed figure consider those eight triple sets (formed out

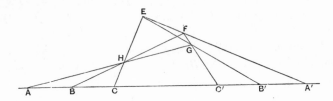

of the six collinear points) which do not contain two members of the same point-pair, then of these the four sets, A, B, C, and A, B', C', and A', B, C', and A', B', C, are such that the three sides of the quadrangle $EFGH$ through any set are concurrent in one of the angular points of the quadrilateral ; while the four sets, A', B', C', and A', B, C, and A, B', C, and A, B, C', are such that the three sides through any set form a triangle. Let any member of the first four sets be called a 'copunctual' set, and let any member of the second four sets be called a 'triangular' set.

Write $\mathrm{Invol}_q\,(AA',\,BB',\,CC')$ to mean that the three point-pairs (α) are collinear, (β) lie on the pairs of opposite sides of a quadrangle, (γ) and that such a quadrangle can be found for which the triple set $(A,\,B,\,C)$ is copunctual.

23. A special case arises when one point-pair, say C and C', coincide. Then the single point counts as one point-pair. The assertion of the special case will be written in the form Invol_q $(AA',\ BB',\ CC)$. The fundamental theorem is not required for the following propositions.

(a) Harm $(ALDU)$ and Harm $(BLCU)$ imply Invol_q $(AD, BC,\ UU)$.

For (cf. figure) let US and UP be any two lines through SU, and let S be any point on US. Let SA and SB intersect UP in P and Q,

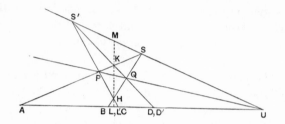

and let CP intersect US in S' and SB in H, and let $S'Q$ intersect SP in K and UA in D'. Let KH intersect US in M and UA in L'. Then $(UBL'C) \overline{\wedge}_H (USMS') \overline{\wedge}_K (UAL'D')$. But Harm $(USMS')$ holds. Hence Harm $(BL'CU)$ and Harm $(AL'D'U)$ hold. Hence from hypothesis L and L' coincide, and thence D and D'.

(β) Invol_q $(AD, BC,\ UU)$ implies that a point L exists such that Harm $(ALDU)$ and Harm $(BLCU)$. This follows at once from the figure of (a).

24. The fundamental theorem is not required for the following propositions.

(a) Invol_q $(AD, BC,\ OU)$ and Invol_q $(AD, BC_1,\ OU)$ imply that C and C_1 coincide.

Firstly let O and U be distinct. Let (as in figure) $SQPS'$ be a quadrangle fulfilling the conditions of Invol_q $(AD, BC,\ OU)$, and let (as in figure) $S_1Q_1P_1S_1'$ be a quadrangle fulfilling those of Invol_q $(AD, BC_1,\ OU)$. Also let $S'C$ and $S_1'C_1$ intersect in C', and SS' and UP in V, and S_1S_1' and UP_1 in V_1. Then by Desargues' Theorem, considering SQS' and $S_1Q_1S_1'$, since B, D, O are collinear, SS_1, $S'S_1'$, QQ_1 are concurrent. Similarly by considering SQV and $S_1Q_1V_1$, since B, U, O are collinear, SS_1, QQ_1, VV_1 are concurrent. Again by considering SPV and $S_1P_1V_1$, since A, U, O are collinear,

SS_1, PP_1, VV_1 are concurrent. Hence the three concurrences are at the same point. Hence SS_1, $S'S_1'$, PP_1 are concurrent; and hence by considering SPS' and $S_1P_1S_1'$, the three points O, A, C' are collinear.

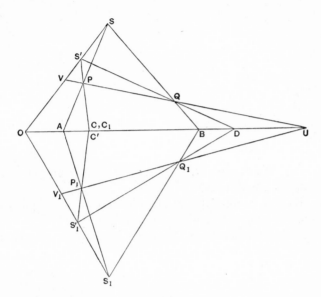

Hence C and C_1 coincide. Secondly let O and U coincide. Then the theorem follows from § 23 (β) and from the uniqueness of the harmonic point.

Corollary. Given five collinear points A, D, B, O, U, there is one and only one point C, such that $\mathrm{Invol}_q\,(AD,\,BC,\,OU)$.

(β) If $\mathrm{Invol}_q\,(AD,\,BC,\,OU)$ holds, a quadrangle can be found fulfilling the conditions with the two sides through O ånd U arbitrarily assumed, and one of the vertices arbitrarily assumed on one of the given sides.

For, whether O and U are or are not distinct, draw any two lines OS and UP through O and U. Take S any point on OS. Join SA and SB, cutting UP in P and Q; and draw DQ cutting OS in S'. Then by (a) $S'P$ passes through C. Hence the theorem is proved.

(γ) $\mathrm{Invol}_q\,(AD,\,BC,\,OU)$ implies $\mathrm{Invol}_q\,(BC,\,AD,\,OU)$, and $\mathrm{Invol}_q\,(DA,\,CB,\,OU)$, and $\mathrm{Invol}_q\,(AD,\,OU,\,BC)$, and so on. This is obvious.

(δ) $\mathrm{Invol}_q\,(AA_1,\,BB_1,\,OU)$ and $\mathrm{Invol}_q\,(A'A_1,\,B'B_1,\,OU)$ imply $\mathrm{Invol}_q\,(AB',\,BA',\,OU)$.

For by (β) the quadrangles can be chosen, as in the figure, to be $SPQS_1$, and S_1PQS'. Then by considering the quadrangle $SPQS'$, the

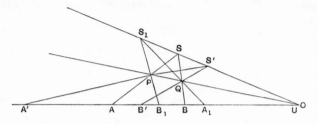

theorem follows. This proof holds whether O and U do or do not coincide.

25. (a) $\mathrm{Invol}_q\,(AD,\,BC,\,OU)$ and $\mathrm{Invol}_q\,(AD,\,BC,\,U_1O)$ imply that U and U_1 are identical.

This theorem requires the fundamental theorem for its proof, or—what is the equivalent—it requires Pappus' Theorem.

For consider the quadrangle $SS'PQ$ which satisfies the conditions

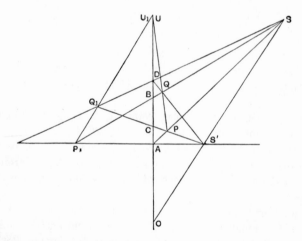

of $\mathrm{Invol}_q\,(AD,\,BC,\,OU)$. Then take P_1 to be the point $(SB\,.\,S'A)$, and Q_1 the point $(SD\,.\,S'C)$.

It follows from § 24 (a) and § 24 (γ) that P_1Q_1 passes through U_1 and that $SS'P_1Q_1$ is a quadrangle satisfying $\mathrm{Invol}_q\,(AD,\,BC,\,U_1O)$. But by considering the hexagon $P_1SADS'Q_1$, it follows from Pappus' Theorem that P, Q, and U_1 are collinear. Hence U and U_1 coincide.

(β) If $\text{Invol}_q (AD, BC, OU)$ and $\text{Invol}_q (AD, BC, U_1O)$ imply that U and U_1 coincide, then the fundamental theorem follows.

This follows at once from the figure of (α). Thus the fundamental theorem and (α) are equivalent.

26. A quadrangular transformation of a line (called the 'axis') into itself is defined thus : Let A, A_1, O, U be four fixed points on the axis, of which O and U may coincide, then a quadrangular transformation of any point X of the axis with the corresponding point X_1 is defined by $\text{Invol}_q (AX_1, XA_1, OU)$.

It follows from the corollary of § 24 (α), that to any point X on the line there is one and only one correspondent. Furthermore it follows from the figure of § 24 (α) that a quadrangular transformation is a projective transformation of the second degree, the 'initial vertex' of projection being (cf. fig. of § 24 (α)) S, the 'final vertex' of projection being S', and UP being the 'auxiliary line' on to which the axis is projected. The line SO is the 'line of vertices.' If O and U coincide the figure of § 23 (α) illustrates the construction.

Furthermore it is evident that any projective transformation of the second degree is a quadrangular transformation.

The points O and U are self-corresponding points in the transformation. By the aid of the fundamental theorem, it can easily be proved that any projective transformation of a line into itself which possesses at least one (real) self-corresponding point is a quadrangular transformation.

The point A, in the above transformation, corresponds to the point A_1. Also the transformation is completely determined by A and A_1, O and U. Furthermore (cf. § 24 (γ) and (δ)) since $\text{Invol}_q (AX_1, XA_1, OU)$ and $\text{Invol}_q (AB_1, BA_1, OU)$ imply $\text{Invol}_q (BX_1, XB_1, OU)$, it follows that any other two corresponding points B and B_1 of the transformation can replace A and A_1. Thus a quadrangular transformation is completely determined by its self-corresponding points (say, O and U) and by the correspondent of any one point (say, A_1 corresponding to A). Such a transformation will be represented by $(AA_1O^2U^2)$. But in the particular case when O and U coincide, the symbol $(AA_1U^2U^2)$ will be replaced by the shorter symbol (AA_1U^2).

A quadrangular transformation, such as (AA_1U^2), with only one self-corresponding point will be called* a 'Prospectivity.'

$(ABC...)$ quad $(A'B'C'...)$ will mean that there is a quadrangular

---

* Cf. Schur, *loc. cit.* Math. Annal. vol. LV.

transformation transforming A to A', B to B', C to C', and so on : also $(ABC\ldots)$ prosp $(A'B'C'\ldots)$ will mean that there is a prospectivity transforming A to A', B to B', C to C'.

(α) $(ABOU)$ quad $(A'B'OU)$ and $(ACOU)$ quad $(A'C'OU)$ implies that $(ABCOU)$ quad $(A'B'C'OU)$.

For in all the cases the quadrangular transformation is the transformation $(AA'O^2U^2)$. This also holds when O and U coincide. Hence we have,

Corollary. (ABU) prosp $(A'B'U)$ and (ACU) prosp $(A'C'U)$ implies $(ABCU)$ prosp $(A'B'C'U)$.

(β) $(ABOU)$ quad (A_1B_1OU), and (A_1B_1OU) quad (A_2B_2OU) implies $(ABOU)$ quad (A_2B_2OU).

For the conditions are Invol_q $(AB_1,\ BA_1,\ OU)$ and Invol_q $(A_1B_2,\ B_1A_2,\ OU)$. Hence (cf. § 24 (δ)) Invol_q $(AB_2,\ BA_2,\ OU)$, that is, $(ABOU)$ quad (A_2B_2OU).

This also holds when O and U coincide. Hence we have,

Corollary. (ABU) prosp (A_1B_1U), and (A_1B_1U) prosp (A_2B_2U) implies (ABU) prosp (A_2B_2U).

(γ) $(AB\ldots)$ quad $(A'B'\ldots)$ implies $(A'B'\ldots)$ quad $(AB\ldots)$. This follows from § 24 (γ).

CHAPTER VI

LINEAR NUMERATION-SYSTEMS

27. Pythagoras is said to have insisted to the verge of mysticism on the fundamental importance of number in forming a conception of the universe. This importance, as we now know, arises from the fact that by the use of the system of positive and negative real numbers all the points of three dimensional space can be systematically named, using four numbers as four names for each point.

Furthermore, and it is here that the importance of the method of naming arises, the names (x, y, z, u) can be so assigned, that a homogeneous indeterminate equation of the first degree represents a plane, and so on.

This method of naming points was first performed by means of the properties of distance, and the Cartesian Geometry resulted. But the converse procedure has now to be established*.

* The germ of the method by which projective coordinates are here introduced was first given by v. Staudt, *Beiträge zur Geometrie der Lage*, 1857, §§ 19, 20, 21, in the calculus of 'Würfen.' These ideas were applied to the problem under consideration by Fiedler, Vierteljahrsschrift der naturforschenden Gesellschaft in Zurich, Bd. xv. 1871, and Lüroth, *Math. Annal.* Bd. viii. 1875, and R. Sturm, *Math. Annal.* Bd. ix. 1876, also Fiedler, *Die Darstellende Geometrie*, 1st Ed. 1871, pp. 505 —580, 3rd Ed. 1888, much enlarged. But in none of the above is the method considered in relation to a very definite system of axioms. The theory is explained at length by Lindemann in his edition of Clebsch's *Vorlesungen über Geometrie*, vol. ii. part 3. The exposition of the method is supplied by Hilbert, *loc. cit.* §§ 24—50, for Descriptive Geometry with a Euclidean axiom. Hilbert's exposition is amplified and completed by Vahlen, *loc. cit.* Both Hilbert and Vahlen consider the question of the introduction of a 'generalized number-system' as coordinates when the Fundamental Theorem and Pappus' Theorem do not hold, in fact the inverse problem of §§ 44—48 below. Hilbert's exposition is applied to Projective Geometry by Schur, *Math. Annal.* Bd. lv. 1902. I have made large use of Schur's memoir. But the subject has admitted of further simplification by the aid of Burali-Forti's investigations, cf. *loc. cit.* § 28 below.

We first indicate the existence of a complete system of magnitudes associated with the points of any segment of a line. By taking any of these magnitudes as an arbitrary unit, the points on the segment are uniquely associated with the positive real numbers; then the points on the complementary segment are associated with the negative real numbers. Thus a one-one relation is established between the points on any arbitrarily assumed line and the whole set of positive and negative real numbers. Three homogeneous coordinates can then be assigned to the points on a given plane, taking an arbitrarily assumed triangle of reference; and thence four homogeneous coordinates to any point in space.

28. The fundamental properties necessary in order to constitute a complete system of magnitudes must first be understood[*].

The symbol + is not otherwise determined than by the assumption that $x + y$ represents the entity, which is arrived at as the result of the operation + upon the two entities x and y, when these entities are of suitable character.

Any class is a 'field' with respect to +, if, when x and y are any members of it, $x + y$ is also a member of it. Assume now that G_0 is a field with respect to +, and let small italic letters, a, b, c, ..., be supposed always to represent members of G_0, unless they are otherwise defined. The null members of G_0 are its members x such that always $a + x = a$. Let G be G_0, exclusive of its null members.

$a > b$, read as 'a is greater than b,' is defined to mean that a member of G, x say, exists such that $a = b + x$. Also $b < a$ means the same as $a > b$; $b < a$ is read as 'b is less than a.'

θa means the subclass of G_0 whose members are all 'less than' a. If u is a subclass of G_0, θu means the class of members of G_0 each of which has the property of being less than a member of u.

A 'bounded existent' subclass of G_0 is a class which has some members and is such that there exists a member of G_0 greater than any member of this subclass.

* This subject has been exhaustively treated by Burali-Forti, cf. Formulaire de Mathématiques, iv. *Théorie des Grandeurs*, Turin, Edition of 1895, also *Les propriétés formales des opérations algébriques*, Rivista di Matematica, vol. vi. Turin 1899, which is the memoir of which parts are here briefly summarized, also *Sulla teoria generale della grandezza e dei numeri*, Atti dei Accad. R. di Torino, vol. xxxix. 1903. See also E. V. Huntington, A set of Postulates for Real Algebra, *Trans. Amer. Math. Soc.* vol. vi. 1905, especially § 3, Theorem 30.

The upper limit (if it exist) of a bounded existent subclass of G_0, u say, is the single member of G_0, x say, such that $\theta x = \theta u$.

The axioms which must hold, in order to constitute G_0 a complete system of magnitudes in respect to the operation $+$, are as follows :

(1) G_0 is a field with respect to $+$,

(2) $a + b = b + a$,

(3) $a + (b + c) = (a + b) + c$,

(4) $a + c = b + c$, implies $a = b$,

(5_1)   At least one null member of G_0 exists,

(5_2)   At least one member of G exists,

(6)   If a is a member of G, $a + b$ is a member of G,

(7)   Either $a = b$, or, $a < b$, or, $a > b$,

(8)   If a is a G, then at least one member of θa is a G,

(9)   Every bounded existent subclass of G_0 possesses an upper limit.

Axiom (9) may be called the Dedekind axiom and should be carefully compared with the Geometrical Dedekind axiom given above.

It can now be proved that there is one unique null member of G_0 : call it 0_+. Also if $a + b = 0_+$, then, $a = 0_+$, and, $b = 0_+$; and if $a + b \neq 0_+$, then either $a \neq 0_+$, or, $b \neq 0_+$. The ordinary elementary properties of $+$ and $>$ and $<$ can now also be proved.

Again the following definitions are made, $0x$ stands for 0_+, $1x$ for x, $2x$ for $x + x$, and so on. These are the multiples of x.

The 'principle of Archimedes' is proved, namely that there always exists an integer m such that $ma > b$; and the existence of submultiples is proved, namely that if m is any integer there always exists one unique member of G_0, x say, such that $mx = a$.

If r is the rational number m/n, then ra is defined to be that single member of G, x say, such that $nx = ma$.

Let s be any (positive) real number ; let u be the class of rational numbers less than s, and with s as its upper limit ; and let ua denote the class of members of G_0 expressible in the form ra, where r is a member of u. Then sa is that member of G_0 which is the upper limit of the class ua. Then if s and t are any (positive) real numbers, it can be proved that

$$sa + ta = (s + t)\, a, \qquad sa + sb = s\,(a + b), \qquad s\,(ta) = (st)\, a.$$

Finally, taking any member of G, a say, as the 'unit' of magnitude, any other member of G can be expressed uniquely in the form sa, where s is some appropriate real number. Thus with each member of G_0, a real number s is uniquely associated.

29. Continuing the suppositions of the previous article (§ 28), subtraction is defined thus ; when $b > a$, $b - a$ is the single member of G_0, x say, such that $a + x = b$. The ordinary properties of subtraction can now be proved, remembering that negative quantities have received no definition.

It is now easy to see the conditions necessary for a class to form a complete system of positive and negative quantities. Let the class g satisfy the axioms (1) to (5) with respect to the operation $+$; also let g be divisible into two exclusive classes $\overline{G}$ and G_0, and let G_0 satisfy all the axioms (1) to (9), and let G be the subclass of G_0, exclusive of the null element 0_+. Finally let there be a one-one correlation between the members G and $\overline{G}$, so that if x and x' are any pair of correlates, $x + x' = 0_+$. Then the ordinary theory holds for members of the class $\overline{G}$; and if a and b are any two members of g, $a - b$ has a meaning in all cases.

Also $\overline{G}$ together with 0_+ also satisfies all the axioms (1) to (9). The symbols $>$ and $<$ now want defining afresh in order to preserve their usual uniform meaning throughout the whole of g.

The whole system of positive and negative real numbers can now be associated by a one-one correspondence with the various members of g, when any member a of G has been taken as an arbitrary unit.

30. Prospectivities on the same line with the same self-corresponding point will now be proved to have the properties of a system of magnitudes.

Definition. $(ABU^2) + (CDU^2)$ is the transformation which results from first applying the prospective transformation (ABU^2) and then applying the prospective transformation (CDU^2).

(a) $(ABU^2) + (CDU^2)$ is itself a prospectivity. This follows immediately from § 26 (β). Thus if it transforms F to G, we have

$$(FGU^2) = (ABU^2) + (CDU^2).$$

But we shall usually find it convenient to represent prospectivities by reference to a given 'initial' point O, thus prospectivities will be written as (OAU^2), (OBU^2), and so on.

(β) $(OCU^2) = (OAU^2) + (OBU^2)$ is equivalent to Invol_q $(OC, AB, UU)^*$.

For (cf. § 24 (β)) in the figure S and S_1 are the initial vertices of the prospectivity (OAU^2), and S and S_2 of the prospectivity (OBU^2).

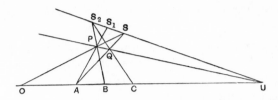

Then it follows immediately from the figure, by considering the quadrangle SS_2PQ, that, $(OCU^2) = (OAU^2) + (OBU^2)$, implies Invol_q (OC, AB, UU).

Again, if the quadrangle SS_2PQ is constructed as in the figure, with its sides through O and C, A and B, U and U, then drawing APS_1, we see at once that Invol_q (OC, AB, UU) implies

$$(OCU^2) = (OAU^2) + (OBU^2).$$

(γ) $(OCU^2) = (OAU^2) + (OBU^2)$ is equivalent to (OAU) prosp (BCU), and also to (OBU) prosp (ACU).

This follows at once from (β).

The property expressed by $(OAU^2) + (OBU^2) = (OCU^2)$ is projective. For it expresses the existence of a certain plane figure in relation to O, A, B, C, U, with properties which can be wholly expressed in terms of collineations and intersections of lines. But such properties are projective. Thus if r be any projective transformation and the correlate of any point P is P_r, we have $(OAU^2) + (OBU^2) = (OCU^2)$, implies $(O_rA_rU_r^2) + (O_rB_rU_r^2) = (O_rC_rU_r^2)$.

31.   (α) $(OAU^2) + (OBU^2) = (OBU^2) + (OAU^2)$.

This follows at once from § 24 (γ) and § 30 (β).

(β) $\{(OAU^2) + (OBU^2)\} + (OCU^2)$
$$= (OAU^2) + \{(OBU^2) + (OCU^2)\}.$$

For put, using § 30 (α),

$$(OAU^2) + (OBU^2) = (OC_1U^2) \quad \ldots\ldots\ldots\ldots\ldots\text{I.}$$
$$(OBU^2) + (OCU^2) = (OA_1U^2) \quad \ldots\ldots\ldots\ldots\text{II.}$$
$$(OC_1U^2) + (OCU^2) = (ODU^2) \quad \ldots\ldots\ldots\ldots\text{III.}$$
$$(OAU^2) + (OA_1U^2) = (OD'U^2) \quad \ldots\ldots\ldots\ldots\text{IV.}$$

---

* Cf. Schur, *loc. cit.* Math. Annal. vol. LV.

Then from I and IV and § 30 (β), we have

$\mathrm{Invol_q} \, (OC_1, \, AB, \, UU)$ and $\mathrm{Invol_q} \, (OD', \, AA_1, \, UU)$.

Hence by § 24 (δ) we have

$$\mathrm{Invol_q} \, (C_1A_1, \, BD', \, UU) \quad \dots\dots\dots\dots\dots \text{V.}$$

Similarly from II and III and § 30 (β) and § 24 (δ), we have

$$\mathrm{Invol_q} \, (C_1A_1, \, BD, \, UU) \quad \dots\dots\dots\dots\dots \text{VI.}$$

Hence from V and VI and § 24 (α), D and D' coincide.

(γ) $(OAU^2) + (OCU^2) = (OBU^2) + (OCU^2)$, implies

$$(OAU^2) = (OBU^2).$$

For (cf. § 26 (β)) we may put

$$(ODU^2) = (OAU^2) + (OCU^2) = (OBU^2) + (OCU^2).$$

Hence (cf. § 30 (β)) we have $\mathrm{Invol_q} \, (OD, \, AC, \, UU)$, and $\mathrm{Invol_q}$ $(OD, \, BC, \, UU)$. Hence (cf. § 24 (α) and § 24 (γ)) A and B coincide.

(δ) The prospectivity (OOU^2) has the 'null' property. For whatever point on the line A may be, we have

$$(OOU^2) + (OAU^2) = (OAU^2).$$

32. (ABU) prosp $(A'B'U)$ implies that $(AA'U)$ S-concord $(BB'U)$, and (ABU) S-concord $(A'B'U)$.

For let $(ABCDA'U)$ prosp $(A'B'C'D'A''U)$. Then by the projectivity of S-concordance (cf. § 17), we have (cf. § 26) (ABU) S-concord (CDU) is equivalent to $(A'B'U)$ S-concord $(C'D'U)$.

Hence, since S-concordance and S-discordance (cf. § 15) are the only alternatives,

$$(ABU) \; S\text{-concord} \; (A'B'U) \text{ is equivalent to}$$
$$(CDU) \; S\text{-concord} \; (C'D'U) \dots\dots\dots\dots\dots(1).$$

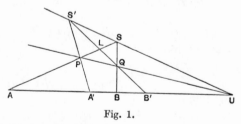

Fig. 1.

Again (cf. fig. 1 and § 21)

$$(AA'B'U) \; \overline{\wedge}_{S'} \, (APLS) \; \overline{\wedge}_{Q} \, (AUB'B) \; \overline{\wedge} \, (B'BAU).$$

Hence by the projectivity of S-concordance

$$(AA'U) \; S\text{-concord} \; (A'B'U) \text{ is equivalent to}$$

$$(B'BU) \; S\text{-concord} \; (BAU),$$

that is to $$(BB'U) \; S\text{-concord} \; (ABU).$$

Hence, as before,

$$(AA'U) \; S\text{-concord} \; (BB'U) \text{ is equivalent to}$$
$$(ABU) \; S\text{-concord} \; (A'B'U) \quad \dots\dots\dots\dots(2).$$

Thus from (1) and (2), it follows that the following five propositions are equivalent, *i.e.* all true or all false, namely,

$$(AA'U) \; S\text{-concord} \; (BB'U),$$
$$(CC'U) \; S\text{-concord} \; (DD'U),$$
$$(AA'U) \; S\text{-concord} \; (A'A''U),$$
$$(ABU) \; S\text{-concord} \; (A'B'U),$$
$$(CDU) \; S\text{-concord} \; (C'D'U).$$

Call this result (3).

But (cf. fig. 2),

$$(AA'A''U) \; \overline{\wedge}_L \; (PNQU) \; \overline{\wedge}_{A'} \; (S'MSU) \; \overline{\wedge}_L \; (A''A'AU).$$

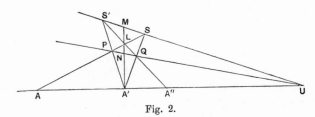

Fig. 2.

Hence $$(AA''U) \; S\text{-concord} \; (AA'U) \text{ is equivalent to}$$
$$(A''AU) \; S\text{-concord} \; (A''AU),$$
i.e. to $(AA''U) \; S\text{-concord} \; (A'A''U)$.

Hence by the theory of the two alternatives,

$$(AA'U) \; S\text{-concord} \; (A'A''U) \text{ is equivalent to}$$
$$(AA''U) \; S\text{-concord} \; (AA''U).$$

But this last theorem of the two equivalents is true.   Hence
$(AA'U) \; S\text{-concord} \; (A'A''U)$ is true.

Hence all the results of (3) follow.

Note that the present article is the first article since § 21, inclusive, in which the geometrical axioms of order, viz. axioms XVI, XVII, XVIII, have been required, except so far as they are required to establish the fundamental theorem which was used in § 25.

33.   (α) $(OCU^2) = (OAU^2) + (OBU^2)$,   implies   that (OBU) *S*-concord (ACU), and (OAU) *S*-concord (BCU).

This follows at once from § 30 (γ) and § 32.

(β) Hence if B lies in segm (OAU), then, with the hypothesis of (α), C also lies in segm (OAU), and follows A in the *S*-order (OAU).

(γ) Again if C lies in segm (OAU) and follows A in the *S*-order (OAU), there is a point B in segm (OAU) such that

$$(OAU^2) + (OBU^2) = (OCU^2).$$

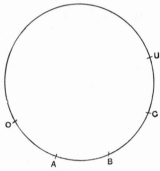

34. (α) Now consider the class, g say, of prospectivities on a given line, with a given self-corresponding point U.

Take O and E any two arbitrarily assumed points on the line, distinct from U and from each other. Then any prospectivity of the class g can be written in the form (OPU^2), where P is any point on the line. Now let G_0 be the subclass of g formed by prospectivities (OPU^2), when P is either in the segm (OEU^2), or coincides with O.

Then, assuming the determination of the meaning of + given in § 30, the class g satisfies axioms (1) to (5) of § 28 [cf. § 30 (α), § 31 (α), § 31 (β), § 31 (γ), § 31 (δ)]. Also G_0 satisfies all the nine axioms of § 28 [cf. § 33 (β), § 33 (γ)]. Axiom (9) is proved by noticing that from § 33 (α), and axiom XVIII of § 19, the upper limit of a bounded existent class of G_0 always exists.

The class $\overline{G}$ is the class g, exclusive of the subclass G_0. Thus $\overline{G}$ is composed of prospectivities (OPU^2), where P lies in segm $(O\hat{E}U)$.

(β) Now consider two points A and A' connected by

$$(OAU^2) + (OA'U^2) = (OOU^2).$$

Then the annexed figure shews that Harm $(AOA'U)$ is the necessary and sufficient condition. Thus all the conditions of § 29 are now satisfied.

Hence taking (OEU^2) as an arbitrary unit, each prospectivity of g, and hence each point of the line, is uniquely associated with a real number; and conversely all the real numbers, positive and negative, are thus exhausted.

In this way O is associated with 0, E with 1, and U with ∞ ; also the order of the real numbers agrees (cf. § 33) with the order of the points on the line, taken in the sense (OEU).

Let the 'numeration-system $[OEU]$' denote the above method of

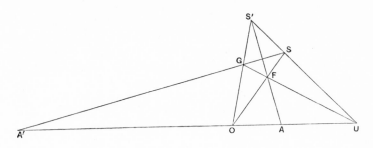

assigning real numbers to points on the line OEU, where O is the 'zero point,' E the 'unit point,' and U the 'infinity point.'

35. The investigation of the present article is interesting, though unconnected with the strict logic of our immediate investigation.

The set of real numbers of the form $m/2^n$, where m and n are integers, is everywhere dense among the positive real numbers. Now in the numeration-system $[OEU]$ any point whose number is of this form can be constructed by a finite number of steps.

(a) For if P be the point with the number x, the point P_m, corresponding to mx, is constructed by

$$(OP_m U^2) = (OP U^2) + (OP U^2) + \dots \text{ to } m \text{ terms.}$$

This represents a finite number of constructions.

(β) Again let G be the point which corresponds to any real number x in the numeration-system $[OEU]$, then the point corresponding to $\tfrac{1}{2}x$ can be constructed.

For (cf. figure) take S_1 and S_2 collinear with U, and P and Q collinear with U, and G_2 on the axis, so that

$$(OGU) \overline{\wedge}_{S_1} (PQU) \overline{\wedge}_{S_2} (GG_2U).$$

Thus $(OGU^2) = (GG_2U^2)$.

Let PG_2 cut S_1S_2 in S_1', and QG in L. Then considering the quadrangle PGG_2Q, we find that Harm $(S_2S_1US_1')$. Let UL cut OS_1 in M, and OS_2 in N; and let S_2M cut OU in F.

Now considering the quadrangle $GLPM$, ML passes through U, GP through S_2, MP and GL through S_1, and PL through S_1'. Hence MG passes through S_1'.

Again, considering the quadrangle $OFMN$, we see that NF passes through S_1'.

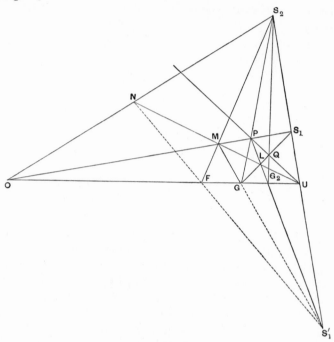

Hence finally, $(OFU) \overline{\wedge}_{S_2} (NMU) \overline{\wedge}_{S_1'} (FGU)$.

Thus $(OFU^2) + (OFU^2) = (OGU^2)$,

and therefore F is the point $\frac{1}{2}x$.

(γ) Thus, using (β) and starting from the point E which corresponds to 1, by n successive constructions the point $1/2^n$ is constructed, where n is any integer. Hence by the use of (α) the point $m/2^n$ is finally constructed. Points corresponding to positive real numbers of this form are everywhere dense in segm (OEU); and the corresponding harmonic points with respect to O and U are everywhere dense in segm $(O\hat{E}U)$.

CHAPTER VII

COORDINATES

36. (a) In the numeration-system $[OEU]$, let O' correspond to the real number a, and E' to the real number b. Also let P correspond to x in the numeration-system $[OEU]$, and to x' in the numeration-system $[O'E'U]$. To prove that

$$x = a + (b - a)\,x'.$$

For

$$(OPU^2) = (OO'U^2) + (O'PU^2)\ldots(1).$$

But by hypothesis

$$(OPU^2) = x(OEU^2),$$

$$(O'PU^2) = x'(O'E'U^2)\ldots(2).$$

Now

$$(O'PU^2) = (OPU^2) + (O'OU^2)$$

$$= (OPU^2) - (OO'U^2) \quad\ldots\ldots\ldots\ldots\ldots(3),$$

and

$$(O'E'U^2) = (OE'U^2) - (OO'U^2)$$

$$= b\,(OEU^2) - a\,(OEU^2)$$

$$= (b - a)\,(OEU^2) \quad\ldots\ldots\ldots\ldots\ldots(4).$$

Thus from (1), (2), (3), (4),

$$x\,(OEU^2) = a\,(OEU^2) + (b - a)\,x'\,(OEU^2).$$

Hence $x = a + (b - a)\,x'$.

(β) Since (cf. § 30 (δ)) the property expressed by the addition of prospectivities is projective, if the range $(OEUP)$ is projective with the range $(O'E'U'P')$, then the number corresponding to P in the numeration-system $[OEU]$ is the same as that corresponding to P' in the numeration-system $[O'E'U']$.

37. (a) Coordinates can be assigned as follows to any point P on a plane. Take any triangle OUV, and any point E_1 on OU, and any point E_2 on OV. Let VP intersect OU in M, and UP intersect

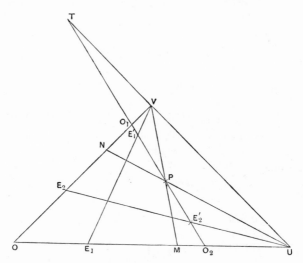

OV in N. Let x be the number assigned to M by the numeration-system $[OE_1U]$, and y the number assigned to N by the numeration-system $[OE_2V]$, then x and y are the coordinates of P.

(β) It is now necessary to prove that the equation of a straight line is linear. First consider a line not passing through U, or V. Let P (x, y) be any point on it. Let the line cut OU, OV, UV in O_2, O_1, T respectively, and also cut VE_1 in E_1' and UE_2 in E_2'.

Then by § 36 (β) above x is the number assigned to P by the numeration-system $[O_1E_1'T]$, and y is the number assigned to P by the numeration-system $[O_2E_2'T]$. Hence by § 36 (a) we have a relation of the form

$$y = mx + c$$

as the equation of the line O_1O_2T.

Secondly if the line passes through U or V, it follows from (a) that the equation is of the form

$$y = b, \text{ or, } x = a.$$

(γ) According to this assignment of coordinates, the coordinates of any point on UV are (∞, ∞).

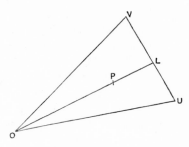

But the coordinates of any point P, other than L, on the line OL, are in a constant ratio (cf. (β)). Thus the infinities on UV may be avoided, (1) by taking the coordinates of L to be in the same constant ratio as those of any other point P on OL, (2) by writing ξ/ζ, η/ζ for x and y, and taking $\zeta = 0$ to be the equation of the line VU.

38. (a) Assigning the homogeneous coordinates of points in a given plane as in § 37 (γ), let a, b, c and a', b', c' be the homogeneous coordinates of two points A and A'. Then the coordinates of any point (θ, ϕ) on the line AA' can be written $\theta a + \phi a'$, $\theta b + \phi b'$, $\theta c + \phi c'$. The anharmonic ratio of a range of four such points, viz. $[(\theta_1, \phi_1),$ $(\theta_2, \phi_2), (\theta_3, \phi_3), (\theta_4, \phi_4)]$, is defined to be

$$(\theta_1\phi_2 - \theta_2\phi_1)(\theta_3\phi_4 - \theta_4\phi_3)/(\theta_1\phi_4 - \theta_4\phi_1)(\theta_3\phi_2 - \theta_2\phi_3).$$

Then by the ordinary processes of analytical geometry, it is proved that the equality of the two anharmonic ratios is the necessary and sufficient condition that the two ranges $(P_1P_2P_3P_4)$ and $(Q_1Q_2Q_3Q_4)$ should be projective.

(β) Hence attending to the generation of homogeneous coordinates, as in § 37 (γ), from two numeration-systems, viz. on OV and OU (cf. fig. § 37 (a)), it follows that if the range $(P_1P_2P_3P_4)$ on the axis OU corresponds to (x_1, x_2, x_3, x_4) in the numeration-system $[OEU]$, and on the same axis OU the range $(Q_1Q_2Q_3Q_4)$ to (y_1, y_2, y_3, y_4) in the same numeration-system, then the necessary and sufficient condition for

$$(P_1P_2P_3P_4) \; \overline{\wedge} \; (Q_1Q_2Q_3Q_4)$$

is $(x_1 - x_2)(x_3 - x_4)/(x_1 - x_4)(x_3 - x_2) = (y_1 - y_2)(y_3 - y_4)/(y_1 - y_4)(y_3 - y_2).$

Define $(x_1 - x_2)(x_3 - x_4)/(x_1 - x_4)(x_3 - x_2)$ to be the anharmonic ratio of the range $(P_1P_2P_3P_4)$ in the numeration-system $[OEU]$.

(γ) Note that it has yet to be proved that the anharmonic ratio as thus defined is the same for every numeration-system on the line. When this proposition has been proved, it will follow (cf. § 41) as a corollary that the anharmonic ratio as defined in (a) is the same for any fundamental triangle OUV in the plane, and for any 'unit' points E_1 and E_2 in OU and OV.

39. (a) Consider ranges on a given axis referred to a given numeration-system $[OEU]$. Now any two harmonic ranges are projective (cf. § 9 (δ)); hence cf. § 38 (β) the anharmonic ratios in the numeration-system $[OEU]$ of all harmonic ranges on the axis are equal.

Now let E' correspond to -1 in the numeration-system $[OEU]$. Then (cf. § 34 (β)) we have Harm $(OEUE')$. But the anharmonic ratio of this range is -1. Hence the anharmonic ratio of all harmonic ranges is -1.

(β) Now let P and Q be such that Harm $(EPE'Q)$, and let x correspond to P, and y to Q in the numeration-system $[OEU]$. Then from (a) we find, $xy = 1$.

(γ) But with P and Q as in (β), we have

$$(OEUQP) \,\overline{\wedge}\, (UEOPQ).$$

Hence (cf. § 36 (β)) since numeration-systems are projective, we find that if x corresponds to P in the numeration-system $[OEU]$, then $\dfrac{1}{x}$ corresponds to P in the numeration-system $[UEO]$.

40. (a) We can now consider the effect of shifting U to U', where U' corresponds to c in the numeration-system $[OEU]$.

Let P correspond to x in the numeration-system $[OEU]$ and to x' in the numeration-system $[OEU']$. Then (cf. § 39 (γ)) P corresponds to $\dfrac{1}{x}$ and U' to $1/c$ in the numeration-system $[UEO]$, and (cf. § 36 (a)) P to $\dfrac{c-x}{(c-1)\,x}$ in the numeration-system $[U'EO]$, and (cf. § 39 (γ)) to $\dfrac{(c-1)\,x}{c-x}$ in the numeration-system (OEU').

(β) In the numeration-system (OEU) let O' correspond to a, E' to b, and U' to c. Also let P correspond to x in the numeration-system $[OEU]$ and to x' in the numeration-system $[O'E'U']$. Then, from (a) and from § 36 (a),

$$x' = \frac{(b-c)\,(x-a)}{(b-a)\,(x-c)}.$$

(γ) It follows immediately from (β) that the anharmonic ratios of any range on a given axis in all the numeration-systems on that axis are equal. Thus the reference to the particular numeration-system may be omitted in the specification of an anharmonic ratio.

(δ) Considering any range $(P_1P_2P_3P_4)$, let x correspond to P_4 in the numeration-system $(P_3P_2P_1)$. Then, from § 38 (β) and § 40 (γ), x is the anharmonic ratio of the range $(P_1P_2P_3P_4)$.

41. Let the homogeneous coordinates ξ, η, ζ of any point P on a given plane be arrived at as in § 37 (γ), where OUV is the fundamental triangle. Make the linear transformation

$$\xi = a_1 x + b_1 y + c_1 z,$$
$$\eta = a_2 x + b_2 y + c_2 z,$$
$$\zeta = a_3 x + b_3 y + c_3 z\ ;$$

where the determinant of the transformation is not zero.

Then the three equations $x = 0$, $y = 0$, $z = 0$ determine respectively the three lines BC, CA, AB. Referred to x, y, z as new coordinates

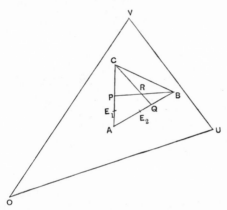

the points A, B, C are respectively the points $(a, 0, 0)$, $(0, \beta, 0)$, $(0, 0, \gamma)$, where a, β, γ may be given any arbitrary values. The coordinates of any point P on AC are $(a, 0, \theta\gamma)$. Let E_1 be the point $(a, 0, \gamma)$.

Then the number corresponding to P in the numeration-system $[AE_1C]$ is the anharmonic ratio of (CE_1AP), that is, θ. Similarly $(a, 0, \phi\beta)$ is any point Q on AB, and E_2 is the point $(a, 0, \beta)$, and ϕ is the number corresponding to Q in the numeration-system $[AE_2B]$. Thus as in § 37 (γ) the coordinates of the point R, where BP and CQ intersect, can be taken to be x', y', z', where $y'/x' = \theta$, and $y'/x = \phi$.

But in terms of the new coordinates (x, y, z) derived from the algebraic transformation, the equation of the line BP is $z/x = \theta\gamma/a$, and of CQ is $y/x = \phi\beta/a$.

Hence the coordinates (x, y, z) derived from algebraic transformation can be identified with those obtained from ABC by the method of § 37 (γ), by putting $a = \beta = \gamma$, or, as is easily seen, by the proper choice of E_1 and E_2 when a, β, γ are given.

42. (α) The assignment of coordinates in three dimensions is conducted in a similar manner.

Let $OUVW$ be any tetrahedron, and P any point whatever. Let UP meet the plane OVW in Q, VP the plane OWU in R, and WP

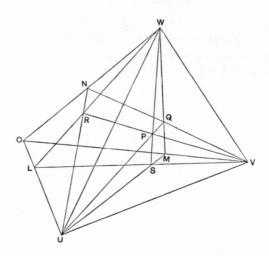

the plane OUV in S. Also VS and WR intersect in L on OU, US and WQ in M on OV, UR and VQ in N on OW.

Now on OU, OV, OW take arbitrary fixed points E_1, E_2, E_3. Let x, y, z be the numbers assigned respectively to L, M, N by the systems $[OE_1U]$, $[OE_2V]$ and $[OE_3W]$. Then x, y, z are the coordinates of P.

These are made homogeneous by writing x/u, y/u, z/u for x, y, z respectively, and by applying reasoning similar to that in § 37 (γ).

(β) The equation of a plane is of the first degree. For first consider a plane not containing any of the corners of the fundamental tetrahedron $OUVW$. Let it cut OU in H_1, OV in H_2, OW in H_3, VW in K_1, WU in K_2, UV in K_3. Also let P, coordinates (x, y, z, u), be any point on it.

Then $(OVW) \overline{\wedge}_U (H_1K_3K_2)$. Hence, referred to the triangle $H_1K_3K_2$, the coordinates of P are y, z, u.

Again $(OUW) \overline{\wedge}_V (H_2K_3K_1)$. Hence, referred to the triangle $H_2K_3K_1$, the coordinates of P are x, z, u. Hence by the theory of the transformation of coordinates (cf. § 41), we find a relation of the form

$$x = ay + bz + cu.$$

It is impossible to find other distinct relations of this form by projecting from W. For if two such relations exist, by elimination a relation of the form, $\alpha y + \beta z + \gamma u = 0$, can be found. But (cf. fig. of (α)) the coordinates y, z, u of P are the same as the coordinates y, z, u of Q. Hence the above relation holds between the coordinates of Q. But Q is any point on the plane OVW, while (cf. § 37 (β)) the relation between y, z, u is characteristic of a single straight line on OVW. Hence two linear relations between x, y, z, u cannot hold for any point on a plane.

Secondly, the above reasoning holds if the restriction that the plane does not possess any of the points O, U, V, W is reduced to the statement that it does not possess more than one of the points U, V, W.

Thirdly, let the plane contain V and W, for instance let it be the plane VLW of the fig. of (α), then the x/u of P is the x/u of L. Hence $x = du$ is the equation of the plane. Also the equation of the plane UVW is $u = 0$.

CHAPTER VIII

EXISTENCE THEOREMS

43. (*a*) The Dedekind Axiom (cf. § 19) is independent of the other axioms. For consider the complete geometry, as we have now deduced it, in which each point is denoted by four homogeneous coordinates (x, y, z, u), their ratios only being relevant. From this complete set of points select those capable of representation by four rational coordinates. Then the equation of any plane containing three such points can be written,

$$lx + my + nz + pu = 0,$$

where l, m, n, p are rational numbers. Call these points the 'rational points,' and these planes the 'rational planes.' A rational line is the intersection of two rational planes. Then any two rational points lie on a rational line, and any two rational lines intersect in a rational point. All the axioms, with the exception of the Dedekind axiom, are satisfied in a Geometry restricted to these points and lines. Furthermore the Fundamental Theorem also holds; and the rational points on any rational line form a compact closed series.

(β) The existence theorem* for the complete set of axioms, I—XIX, with the modification of XV into an axiom restricting the number of dimensions to any finite integral number, $n-1$, can be proved as follows: Let the n positive or negative real numbers (x_1, x_2, ... x_n) be considered as the name of a point, where x_1, x_2, ... x_n are not all zero, and (px_1, px_2, ... px_n), where p is any real number not zero, names the same point as (x_1, x_2, ... x_n). A straight line is defined to be the set of points satisfying $n-2$ independent homogeneous linear equations involving x_1, x_2, ... x_n as unknowns.

Then all the axioms are satisfied provided that we can specify the set of entities which (x_1, x_2, ... x_n), for the various determinations of (x_1, x_2, ... x_n) can be conceived to name. Now (x_1, x_2, ... x_n) can be

---

* Cf. Russell, *Principles of Mathematics*, § 413 and § 360 [note misprint 'real' for 'complex' in line 21 of § 360].

taken as naming a certain many-one relation between all the n integers 1, 2, ... n and some of the real numbers, namely that many-one relation which correlates 1 to x_1, 2 to x_2, ... and n to x_n. Thus the point (x_1, x_2, x_3, x_4) is the class of correlations of which any typical member is named by (ax_1, ax_2, ax_3, ax_4), where $a \neq 0$. Accordingly the complete set of points is the complete set of classes of all such correlations.

Hence if a purely logical definition can be given of the set of real numbers, and if the set of real numbers as thus defined can be proved from purely logical premises to possess the properties ordinarily assigned to real numbers in pure mathematics, then the existence theorem for the Projective Geometry based upon Axioms I to XIX, and restricted to n dimensions, has been proved. Thus the vital importance to Pure Mathematics of such a minute logical investigation into the theory of real numbers is obvious*.

44. Hilbert's proof that the Fundamental Theorem cannot be deduced from Axioms I—XV will now be considered. Hilbert† himself has published notes or headings of a proof rather than a proof itself. The following summary is a condensation of a complete proof by Vahlen‡. The preliminary explanations will occupy more than one article.

Consider a class K and two operations + and × with the following properties:

(1) K is a class.

If a, b, and c are members of K, then

(2) $a + b$ is a member of K,

(3) $(a + b) + c = a + (b + c)$,

(4) $a + b = b + a$,

(5) $a + b = a + c$, implies $b = c$,

(6) There is at least one member of K, z say, such that $z + z = z$,

(7) There is a member of K, x say, such that $a + x = b$.

Then it can be proved that there is only one member of K with the property (6). Denote this member by 0. Also, when a and b are any given members of K, there is only one member of K with the

* Cf. Russell, *loc. cit.*, Part II and Part V.
† Cf. *loc. cit.* §§ 31—35.
‡ Cf. *loc. cit.* pp. 1—110.

property of x in (7). Denote by $-a$, the single member of K with the property, $a + (-a) = 0$; and write $a - b$ for $a + (-b)$.

Again make the same supposition that a, b, c are any members of K, also write ab as a shortened form of $a \times b$. Then the following further properties are to hold of K and $+$ and $\times$:

(8) $a(b + c) = ab + ac$,

(9) $(b + c)a = ba + ca$,

(10) $(ab)c = a(bc)$,

(11) If $a \neq 0$, and $ab = ac$, then $b = c$,

(12) If $a \neq 0$, and $ba = ca$, then $b = c$,

(13) There is at least one member of K, z say, such that $zz = z$,

(14) If $a \neq 0$, there is at least one member of K, x say, such that $ax = b$,

(15) If $a \neq 0$, there is at least one member of K, y say, such that $ya = b$.

Then it can be proved that

$$a0 = 0a = 0 ;$$

also that there is one and only one member of K with the property (13). Denote it by 1. Also it can be proved that the equations $ax = b$, and $ya = b$, have each of them only one solution, assuming $a \neq 0$, and $b \neq 0$.

Let a^{-1} be defined to be the single member of K such that $aa^{-1} = 1$. Then it can be proved that $a^{-1}a = 1$. But ba^{-1} must be distinguished from $a^{-1}b$, except when $b = a$.

Let 2, 3, 4, etc. be defined thus: $2 = 1 + 1$, $3 = 2 + 1$, $4 = 3 + 1$, etc. All the members of K which are thus obtained are called the 'integral' members of K. If a is any member of K, and n is any integral member of K, then $na = an$.

The 'rational' members of K are those members of K, r for instance, such that there exist two integral members of K, m and n say, such that $mr = n$. Then if a is any member of K, and r is any rational member of K, $ra = ar$. Evidently the integral members of K are among the rational members of K.

45. These properties, namely (1) to (15) of § 44, do not involve the commutative law for multiplication, namely $ab = ba$, though of course they are consistent with it. This possible existence of a class with the above properties, but excluding the commutative law, can be verified by considering the class of quaternions, excluding imaginary quaternions, but including degenerate quaternions in the form of positive and negative scalars, and the null quaternion. These satisfy all the requisite axioms. It is to be noted that if a and b are any quaternions, then, $ab = ba$, is not in general true.

46. Continue the assumption that K is a class satisfying (1) to (15) of § 44, and that all the non-capital letters of any alphabet and numerals are members of K, as specified in § 44.

Let (x, y, z, u) define an object, which we will call a point.

Here x, y, z, u are not to be all identical with 0; also, if $a \neq 0$, (ax, ay, az, au) defines the same point as (x, y, z, u). Then a point is a class of correlations, similarly to the other points defined in § 43 (β). Then x, y, z, u are the 'coordinates' of the point (x, y, z, u). If x, y, z, u are the coordinates of a point, and satisfy

$$x\xi + y\eta + z\zeta + ur = 0,$$

where ξ, η, ζ, r are not all equal to 0, then the point is said to lie in the plane (ξ, η, ζ, r). Thus the plane (ξ, η, ζ, r) is a class of points. Also the planes (ξ, η, ζ, r) and $(\xi a, \eta a, \zeta a, ra)$ are identical, where $a \neq 0$.

A straight line is defined to be the intersection of two distinct planes. Then it can be proved that three distinct planes intersect either in a line or a point.

Then a line is determined by any two points on it. Also if (x_1, y_1, z_1, u_1) and (x_2, y_2, z_2, u_2) are any two distinct points, any point in the line possessing them both can be expressed in the form $(\lambda_1 x_1 + \lambda_2 x_2, \ \lambda_1 y_1 + \lambda_2 y_2, \ \lambda_1 z_1 + \lambda_2 z_2, \ \lambda_1 u_1 + \lambda_2 u_2)$, and conversely any point whose coordinates can be expressed in this form lies on the line.

Also any three non-collinear points determine a plane. If $(x_1, \dots, \dots, \dots)$, $(x_2, \dots, \dots, \dots)$, $(x_3, \dots, \dots, \dots)$ are three non-collinear points, the coordinates of any point on the plane possessing them can be expressed in the form $(\lambda_1 x_1 + \lambda_2 x_2 + \lambda_3 x_3, \ \dots, \ \dots, \ \dots)$.

Then λ_1, λ_2, λ_3 may be called the coordinates of a point in the plane, referred to the triangle, formed by $(x_1, \dots, \dots, \dots)$, $(x_2, \dots, \dots, \dots)$, $(x_3, \dots, \dots, \dots)$, as the fundamental triangle.

47. (a) It can easily be verified that, with the Geometry of § 46, Axioms I—XII of § 4, and Axiom XIII of § 7 and Axiom XV of § 8 are all verified. Thus in this Geometry Desargues' Theorem holds.

Indeed if the definitions of § 46 be modified so as to reduce the Geometry to two dimensions, it can still be proved* that Desargues' Theorem holds.

(β) Axiom XIV, in Pieri's second form, is also verified.

For let $ABCD$ be any quadrilateral, and F, G, H be the three harmonic points, as in the figure. Take ABC to be the fundamental

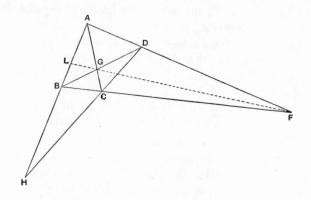

triangle. Then with this assumption, A is $(1, 0, 0)$, B is $(0, 1, 0)$, C is $(0, 0, 1)$, D is (a, β, γ); where no one of a, β, γ is 0. Then since F lies on BC it is of the form $(0, \mu, \nu)$, and since it lies on AD it is of the form $(\theta + \phi a, \phi \beta, \phi \gamma)$. Hence $\theta = -\phi a$. Thus F is $(0, \phi \beta, \phi \gamma)$, that is, $(0, \beta, \gamma)$. Similarly G is $(a, 0, \gamma)$, H is $(a, \beta, 0)$. Thus any point on FG is $\{\phi a, \theta \beta, (\theta + \phi) \gamma\}$. Hence L, where FG and AB intersect is given by $\theta + \phi = 0$. Thus L is $\{a, -\beta, 0\}$. But since β is not 0, β and $-\beta$ are distinct. Hence L and H are distinct. Hence Axiom XIV holds.

48. We can now† prove that Pappus' Theorem does not follow from Axioms I—XV.

Let (cf. fig.) A, B, C and A_1, B_1, C_1 be the two sets of three collinear points. Then we may choose, A to be $(1, 0, 0)$, B to be $(0, 1, 0)$, C to be $(1, \beta, 0)$, A_1 to be $(0, 0, 1)$, B_1 to be (λ, μ, ν), C_1 to be $(\lambda, \mu, 1 + \nu)$; where β, γ, μ, ν are each one not equal to 0.

The above choice of coordinates is consistent with A, B, C and A_1, B_1, C_1 being any six points fulfilling the required conditions.

---

* Cf. Vahlen, *loc. cit.*, Part II, § 84.
† Cf. Vahlen, *loc. cit.*, Part II, § 83 and § 110.

Then D is on BC_1 and on B_1C. Hence it can be expressed in both the forms

$$\{\phi\lambda,\ \theta+\phi\mu,\ \phi(1+\nu)\} \text{ and } \{\xi+\eta\lambda,\ \xi\beta+\eta\mu,\ \eta\nu\}.$$

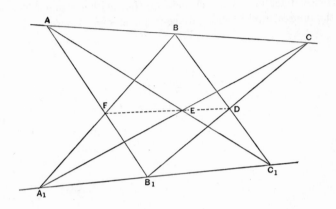

Hence we may put

$$\phi\lambda=\xi+\eta\lambda,\ \theta+\phi\mu=\xi\beta+\eta\mu,\ \phi(1+\nu)=\eta\nu.$$

Thus
$$\eta=\phi\nu^{-1}+\phi\ ;$$

and
$$\phi\lambda=\xi+\phi\nu^{-1}\lambda+\phi\lambda,$$

thus
$$\xi=-\phi\nu^{-1}\lambda.$$

Hence D is the point $\{\lambda,\ \mu+\nu^{-1}\mu-\nu^{-1}\lambda\beta,\ 1+\nu\}$. Similarly E is the point $\{\mu\beta^{-1},\ \mu,\ 1+\nu\}$, and F is the point $(0,\ \mu,\ \nu)$.

Thus any point on EF can be written in the form

$$\{x\mu\beta^{-1},\ (x+y)\mu,\ x+(x+y)\nu\}.$$

If D is such a point, we have the three equations

$$x\mu\beta^{-1}=\lambda \quad\text{...........................(1)},$$

$$(x+y)\mu=\mu+\nu^{-1}\mu-\nu^{-1}\lambda\beta \quad\text{...................(2)},$$

$$x+(x+y)\nu=1+\nu \quad\text{..........................(3)}.$$

Thus from (2) and (3) we find

$$x\nu^{-1}=\nu^{-1}\lambda\beta\mu^{-1}.$$

Substituting this value of x in (1),

$$\nu^{-1}\lambda\beta\mu^{-1}\nu\mu\beta^{-1}=\lambda,$$

that is
$$\lambda\beta\mu^{-1}\nu=\nu\lambda\beta\mu^{-1}.$$

Now put $\delta = \lambda\beta\mu^{-1}$, and we find $\delta\nu = \nu\delta$. Also ν and δ can be any members of K. Thus Pappus' Theorem can only be true when the commutative law for the multiplication of coordinates holds.

Hence it follows from § 11 and § 45 that neither Pappus' Theorem nor the fundamental theorem are consequences of Axioms I—XV.

and hence E is the point of intersection of the line (25) (36) with π.
But E also lies in the intersection of

$$\pi, \quad \{E_5 E_6 (16)(36)\}, \quad \{E_5 E_6 (45)(25)\}.$$

Thus the line (25) (36) must intersect $E_5 E_6$. Hence the two planes

$$\{E_5 E_6 (16)(36)\} \text{ and } \{E_5 E_6 (25)(45)\}$$

are identical; and hence the point (56) exists.

The assumption [as to the existence of (56)] made in the course of the proof of Pappus' Theorem has not been deduced from the preceding axioms. Hilbert* has shown that Pappus' Theorem cannot be deduced from axioms I to XV. Thus the 'fundamental theorem,' or some equivalent theorem, must be assumed as an axiom.

But there is an entirely different line of proof (requiring further axioms) of the fundamental theorem, which may be called 'von Staudt's† continuity proof.'

This proof in its original form contains an oversight, which was first pointed out by Klein‡. The proof will be given here in its amended form. The proof requires that relations of order among points on lines should have been introduced.

Furthermore for the case of Geometries with a finite number of points, it has been shown by J. H. Maclagan-Wedderburn§ that Pappus' Theorem can be proved without any further axioms, beyond the aforesaid one of finiteness of number.

* Cf. *loc. cit.*, chapter VI, and §§ 44 to 48 of this tract.

† Cf. *Geometrie der Lage*, § 9, paragraph 106.

‡ Cf. *Zweiten Aufsatze über nicht-Euclidische Geometrie*, Math. Annal. vol. VI. 1873.

§ Cf. *A Theorem on finite Algebras*, Trans. Amer. Math. Soc. vol. VI. 1905, and *Finite Projective Geometries*, by O. Veblen and W. H. Bussey, Trans. Amer. Math. Soc. vol. VII. 1906, p. 246.

CHAPTER IV

ORDER

13. If A, B, C are three collinear points, the segment ABC—written segm (ABC)—is defined* to be the collection of all collinear points X, such that there is some pair of points y and y' satisfying both Harm $(AyCy')$ and Harm $(ByXy')$. Also segm $(A\hat{B}C)$ is the collection of all points on the line ABC which do not lie on segm (ABC). The extreme instances of the various definitions are so arranged that A and C do not belong to segm (ABC), and that B does belong to segm (ABC).

The basis of these definitions can easily be perceived by considering the Euclidean line made projective by adding in the point at infinity. For if B on such a line lies between A and C, and X is any other point

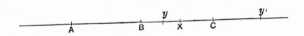

between A and C, then, since pairs of harmonic conjugates separate each other, the two point-pairs A, C and B, X define an involution with real double points, say y and y'. Thus in the Euclidean line, if X be any point in the segment AC in which B also lies, the two points y and y' exist with the property described in the above definition of segm (ABC). Conversely this characteristic property is here taken as the definition.

It can be proved without any further axioms that the propositions, D belongs to segm (ABC), and, B belongs to segm (ADC), imply each other. Also if D lies in segm (ABC) and is distinct from B, then C

* Cf. Pieri, *loc. cit.*